D1003910

Thinking
MATH
Differently

An Essential
FIFTH GRADE Guide
for
Parents AND Teachers

Also part of the **Thinking MATH Differently** *series:*

An Essential KINDERGARTEN Guide

An Essential FIRST GRADE Guide

An Essential SECOND GRADE Guide

An Essential THIRD GRADE Guide

An Essential FOURTH GRADE Guide

Thinking
MATH
Differently

An Essential

FIFTH GRADE Guide

for

Parents AND Teachers

PATTI J. DIECK   CHRISTOPHER M. SARLO

Copyright: 2016

by

CONCEPTUAL LEARNING ASSOCIATES

ISBN: 978-0-9977892-2-5

All Rights Reserved

Printed in the United States of America

<u>*Acknowledgements*</u>

To our loving and infinitely patient spouses, **Mike and Janine**, who put up with our late nights (and subsequently grumpy mornings!) Thank you for your belief in us, your constant encouragement…and for keeping the coffee fresh and freely flowing!

We *FINALLY* finished!!!

To **Matthew** thank you for every late night conversation that ended with, "You've got this, Mom." and to **Jared** for letting your Mom be your "everyday hero".

To **Adam and Lucas,** thank you for your unwavering support, and to **Ava and Olivia** for ALL of your love and excitement surrounding "Our dad's book!"

YES! Let's walk the dog and hang out at the park!

To our amazing parents, *Richard & Janet Petersen and Joseph & Fran Sarlo*, also known as our biggest fans, thank you for always letting us know how proud we make you.

Table of Contents

*NOTE: Please take a few minutes to read "How to Use this Book" before diving into individual math topics. This section contains our recommendations on how to best navigate and use this text, which will ultimately result in maximizing your understanding(s).

Preface

"THIS IS NOT THE MATH I LEARNED! HOW am I supposed to help?"
….Sound familiar??

**THE CURRICULUM CHANGES EVERY YEAR! HOW am I supposed to build on
and lay new foundations?"**
….Sound familiar??

In more than 40 years of combined teaching experience, the first and most-often-asked
question we get from parents is, "How can I help my child?"

Colleagues and other teaching professionals also want something that is "timeless":
strategies and mathematical instructional practices that both transcend
program/curriculum choices and "grow with their students."

With new standards now in effect in almost every state, and similar high standards and
teaching methods driving math instruction in the others, this question, and need for
mathematical understanding has never been timelier.

This guide will help… IRRESPECTIVE of the curriculum or math program your child, or
your school/district employs.

The most important thing today's adults NEED to understand is that we didn't "*learn
different math*" than our children are learning…we just "*learned math differently*".
Everything adults understand about how numbers work and how to use them is still the
same! Wait, let's repeat that… **Everything adults understand about how numbers work
and how to use them is still the same!** The major difference is that we learned "how to
do things" with numbers without learning "why to do them". This process led to the
memorizing of steps rather than simply thinking about what would make sense.
Today's math looks and seems quite confusing to many adults, because teaching
"*understanding*" instead of "*memorization*" is not as straight-forward a process. There are

additional ideas included in the teaching of each topic, which are there to demonstrate the thinking process. To parents these "extra things" often seem confusing, or even unnecessary. But these ideas are **KEYS** to success….and are all specifically pointed out throughout the lessons in this book. What's most important to remember is that our goal for students today is NOT to simply "get the answer"…our goal is for children to understand the processes that lead to the answers. This understanding is what children are then able to USE when faced with similar problems in the real world.

The good news is that there **ARE** simple and practical answers to the questions of how parents can help and how teachers can impact their students' achievement, and this book contains the ones you can use right now. Each learning standard and concept is explained in real, everyday language…finally putting parents and teachers "on the same page"
…and making this guide the perfect companion no matter which curriculum or textbook children use.
As you navigate through the lessons in this book, please keep this thought in mind:

"We don't REMEMBER how to DO math, we THINK about how to USE math to solve problems."

So who are we??

Our incredible journey to this point began PCC (Pre-Common Core)! We have been teaching a combined total of over 40 years in grades 3 through 6, in Suffolk County, New York: Patti 27 years, and Christopher 17 years. A driving force in each of our classrooms has always been the "process of learning"….teaching students to decide what it "makes sense" to do in problem solving situations, and to "puzzle it out" when they aren't immediately sure. It has always been our personal belief that when students learn what it **MEANS** to perform various tasks in mathematics, and when they are taught these concepts through problem solving, they will inherently **KNOW** what to do and how to do it when faced with similar problems. Taking the focus **OFF OF** *finding right answers,* and putting it **ON** *solving problems efficiently and effectively,* makes math thinkers. Teaching algorithms in our classrooms has always been secondary to teaching understanding of what each operation means at its core. In our experience, students who learn this way are far less likely to grow up and become adults who "don't get math". Quite the opposite is true!

It was these beliefs that led to our in-depth knowledge of the Common Core State Standards for Mathematics, and eventually to our work as writers of New York State's Common Core Math Curriculum. (EngageNY.org). Years prior to the implementation of the new standards, New York State commissioned the writing of a new curriculum; one designed and written to meet the standards. A wise decision, given that *no commercially available textbooks had as of yet been adequately revised.* Patti worked as part of the team that produced the grade 4 curriculum, Christopher as part of the grade 5 team. Working with mathematicians and skilled lead writers we helped to craft a curriculum that truly meets the standards, while incorporating the very best teaching strategies.

Our work as consultants and professional development providers was the next logical step, as local school districts suddenly found they needed to provide training for their teachers, who had not learned mathematics this way themselves. To date we have worked with numerous school districts, teacher centers, and yes, Parent Groups! Parents, it seems, are eager, even excited(!), to (finally) learn all of the meaning behind the math they thought was "just a set of steps". The single most-heard comment in all of our parent and teachers workshops is always, "This makes so much sense….I wish we had learned it this way!"

Teaching this way for so many years, and doing so as two of a very few individuals who subscribed to this belief, became increasingly more and more frustrating. We couldn't understand why more teachers did not follow this methodology. We came to understand that a focus on "results" was foremost on most teachers' minds …leading to an overemphasis on procedures and test preparation in most classrooms. What we've realized, and seen demonstrated in the growth scores of our own students, is that our idea of "results" transcends standardized test scores. In fact, the less test prep included in students' daily math instruction, the more they are generally able to demonstrate success and growth on those same standardized tests. As we point out in our training workshops, and as teachers who take those workshops report back to us, it is the *teaching of concepts and the understanding of how numbers work* that yields the best results.

Why did we write this book?

The impetus for this handbook was our desire to help calm the frustration experienced by SO MANY following the implementation of the new math standards. Through our many discussions with professors, administrators, teachers, colleagues, and parents, we learned that most of them have had little or no interaction with math taught this way. Since it's not the way most adults learned themselves, they need to become familiar with the concepts, strategies and vocabulary their children are seeing and interacting with daily.

As two of the writers responsible for the creation the NYS Mathematics Modules (now a National Math Program!) we wholeheartedly believe in the new learning standards. With that said let's outline some pertinent facts that may help you better understand *what exactly is happening*:

- The Common Core State Standards for Mathematics, as well as the new math standards in non-Common Core states, are built on the notion that student **understandings of mathematics** are necessary for finding solutions.
- No matter which curriculum (math series) a school/district uses, there are certain **foundational ideas** they all share. All of today's textbook series were either written or adapted for the same set of learning standards.
- Most problem solving is based on the **use of a model**…children are encouraged to use models to show their thinking. While the models are taught specifically, and one at a time, the big idea is that after learning a variety of models, students will "choose one" that makes sense to them as they work.
- The ultimate goal *is* for students to use "standard algorithms" for the four basic operations (the way we learned!), because standard algorithms ARE easier and

more efficient. The **use of the algorithms** simply comes AFTER the understanding of why they work. Research shows this helps learners remember and use the algorithms more effectively.

- The use of **precise mathematical vocabulary** is a key component to teaching mathematical understanding.
- Modeling and problem solving practice, also known as **application**, have replaced pages of repeated algorithm practice.
- **Fluency with facts** (memorization of addition facts or times tables, for example) is an important component to this learning….it has not been eliminated or replaced.
- Learning **"how numbers behave"** and **"what they can do"** (what today's adults would have learned as the *commutative, associative and distributive properties*) beginning as early as Kindergarten takes students all the way through high school.
- Ultimately if students understand how and why to manipulate numbers, we will **create problem solvers….not "answer getters"**!

What makes this book different?

This book was designed to help you help your children… to take the guesswork out of what each assignment means. Throughout this book you will be introduced to the *big ideas* and main topics studied at each grade level, the *models* used to instruct and foster mathematical thinking for each topic, and the *mathematical vocabulary* used to support learning. You will also learn how each topic relates to grade level learning standards. Finally, this book discusses the *fluency skills* expected to be in place at each grade level in order to ensure success with each concept. All of this information is presented in an easy to follow format that links this new learning to "the way we learned".

HOW TO USE THIS BOOK

This book was written for every adult who has looked at their child's math homework and thought, "HUH?" …or worse, "Good thing I don't have to pass fifth grade again!"

It was written for every teacher who has looked at today's learning standards and thought, "WHAT do they even MEAN??....Where do I START?"

The truth is that today's assignments DO look and feel very different from what almost every adult was taught and is used to. The good news is that even though it looks so different, it's based on the same principles that the math we learned was built on. **"Math"** hasn't changed…**the way we think about it** in the classroom has. Which means that you already know more about this than you thought you did!

Today's math instruction is designed to "directly teach" students a lot of the things we adults had to figure out for ourselves. Let's look at a simple example:

> If we asked you to add 9 to any number, say 35, you would
> probably respond very quickly that the answer is 44.
> Now…THINK for a moment about how you did that so quickly.
> You didn't, we're sure, count on 9 fingers. More than likely you
> simply added 10 to make 45 and then took one off. You knew you
> needed the number 1 less than 45 because 9 is 1 less than 10, **and
> you knew it automatically.**

We're going to go out on a limb here and say that you probably didn't learn this strategy in school. For most adults strategies like this one just developed over time. You probably don't know exactly when you learned that…it's one of those things you do with numbers because **you understand that it makes sense and it will always work.**

THIS is the type of thinking and understanding that's now built into math instruction. Since young learners don't have the experience with numbers we had when we started developing these "makes-sense strategies", they need to be taught how to do it. Teaching children to *understand and apply the way*

2

numbers work looks very different than simply teaching them *what steps to follow*....and THIS is where the trouble starts when it comes to helping children with math assignments. This is also where the stumbling block lies for many teachers. Most of today's teachers learned math "the old way" and so it makes sense to them to teach it that way. They recognize the importance and effectiveness of "this new way" but since they didn't learn this way themselves it's not a simple shift!

So what will you find in this book?...

       ...Everything you need to understand fifth grade math!

Each section of the book represents a major topic of fifth grade math. Within each section are all of the concepts related to that topic, along with the learning standard related to each one. Each standard is explained in **regular "everyday" language**, and is followed by an example. You simply find the concept your child is working on and read the description to understand what the assignment is about. *At times you may need to check out more than one section*. We suggest referencing your child's classwork and then finding the "match" in this book.

We suggest reading through each entire topic, organized as individual chapters, first. Although you may be looking for help teaching or working with one specific concept, it is VERY BENEFICIAL to see how that topic fits into the entire progression of how it is taught. When children are struggling it is often useful for them to see problems presented in alternate or simpler forms. Bringing them "back" to a strategy they have been successful with and showing them how it relates to their current work helps children see the big picture of how it all fits together. It reminds them that they can use what they do know to figure out what they don't. Understanding how each concept "fits" with the others in the topic is what gives adults the insight they need to help it all make sense to children....our prime objective!

The Joys of Problem Solving

Questioning

In addition to the information in the rest of this book, it is also of pivotal importance that you understand the value of asking questions as a way to help your children solve math problems. (Rather than being the source of the answers.) This trains them to think through problems **before** looking for outside assistance. Answering children's questions WITH questions begins in Kindergarten, but becomes much more prominent as children move to later grades. Some problem solving questions may include:

- Do you know the total? (If so then you wouldn't add or multiply.)
- Can you draw a picture? (If so draw it! – "visual representations" often help the problem "make sense".)
- What is happening in the problem/story? (What's the ACTION?)
    - Is there something that is increasing? Decreasing?
    - Does someone/something have more? Less? How much more/less?

The more questions you ask children, which lead to discovering a solution pathway, the better. As parents ourselves, we know that it is MUCH easier, and INFINETLY more efficient, to say something like "just add" or "just subtract". The questioning, however, helps to build conceptual understanding, confidence, independence, and schema.

Asking questions also begins to engage your child in the necessary *internal dialogue* (in their own heads) of problem solving (think about when you try to solve something new, do you often "talk yourself through it?") We want children to develop their own personal strategies for tackling word problems. Whatever their preferred way of doing it is, it MUST make sense to them…MUST be something they can visualize and then puzzle-out….even if it appears to be "the long way" or "more involved" than necessary. Eventually children will develop all of the mental shortcuts we adults employ, but for now letting them develop is the important thing.

©2016 Conceptual Learning Associates

"Key Words"

When solving word problems with your child, try to refrain from pointing out "key words" (words that SEEM to suggest a certain operation). Many adults were taught to look for these words as a first line of attack when solving word problems. The trouble is that these don't always work! Let's look at an example:

> Sam found 15 shells at the beach. He found 9 **more than** his friend Jack. How many shells did Jack find?

Of course, in this case, the answer is 6 shells.

It's common to teach children that the words "more than" suggest a subtraction problem, as we see here. Many children are (mistakenly) taught that when a problem states one number is "more than" another, they should find the difference between the numbers….subtraction.

But let's look at another example:

> Sam found 15 shells at the beach. Jack found 9 **more than** Sam. How many shells did Jack find?

Most adults can "see" the action happening in this problem, and "just know" that the answer is 24. But for children who have been taught to "do what the key words say to do" this is a very confusing problem. It is very difficult for elementary children to both follow the problem solving rules they've been taught, AND do what makes sense when these things don't agree. When problem solving is taught as a following-the-rules activity, THAT is what children will default to. But here, subtraction would lead to an incorrect answer!

Looking for words that "tell us what to do" just doesn't always work. Eventually these "key words" become a hindrance to effective problem solving and do nothing for establishing a conceptual framework of "how numbers work".

Important Terms and Phrases

Throughout this book certain terms and phrases will pop up quite often. Some important ones are defined below. Reading through each of them will help to clarify certain key points as you go through the rest of the book.

> **Learning standards** are a set of guidelines for what students should know, understand, and be able to do at each grade level. This is a major shift from most former sets of state learning standards which were generally just lists of topics teachers needed to cover. Now students must demonstrate an understanding of each concept. In this book each big idea is listed and "translated" into "real, every day" language.

> The **vocabulary and terminology** specific to each big idea are defined and explained. Different math text series often use variations of the same term or idea. Wherever possible, we have included known variations to help you understand the terms that may be included in children's assignments.

> The **models** used to represent each big idea are explained and illustrated. Like the vocabulary terms, models and representations often have different names in different math programs. We have included the more popular names of each model wherever possible. We have also included a picture, diagram or example for how each model is used. The illustration will help you determine which model you may be seeing in children's assignments, even if they are called something else.

Students are exposed to the use of models for problem solving and understanding complex math concepts beginning in Kindergarten. They are taught how, and encouraged, to use models to represent math problems before solving them. While this modeling may seem like an "extra thing to do", research has shown that these models actually create

©2016 Conceptual Learning Associates

"mental scaffolding" allowing students to easily concentrate on and attach new learning to things they already know. Models are introduced early, and reappear throughout each grade level's topics, with students learning new and more complex ways to use them.

➤ Students demonstrate **conceptual understanding** when they know which mathematical ideas are important for solving a problem, why these ideas are important, how an idea or procedure can be explained or justified in its use, and how to adapt previous mathematical experiences to new problem solving situations. In other words, they have a strong sense of numbers, how they work, and the skills they bring to each problem solving situation.

➤ An **algorithm** is a series of "steps" performed in a certain sequence, in order to complete a math calculation. The "standard algorithm" is usually thought of as "the way we learned". It's important to note that today's learning standards still require students to be able to calculate using these algorithms, they simply require students to understand why the algorithms work before being formally introduced to them.

➤ The term **fluency** applies to things students need to "be fluent" in. "Fluent" in the Standards means "fast and accurate." It is similar to what we mean when we say somebody is fluent in a foreign language: when you're fluent, you flow....no time is needed to mentally rehearse; recall of necessary skills and facts is automatic. In other words, students can perform calculations and solve simple problems quickly and accurately. Required fluencies at each grade level build from student understandings in prior grades. For example, third grade students are required by the standards to "fluently multiply and divide within 100"...this means that in second grade students began the foundational work needed to conceptually understand multiplication.

The information found in this book can, and should, be shared with students. Discovery of the purpose behind what is being done may help some children gain a better understanding when applying this knowledge. Older students will benefit from USING this handbook; they should have one to keep in class, and reference it as they work!

Teachers should keep a copy on their desks as a reference in their daily practice as well as in their planning. This will be useful irrespective of the curriculum (text series) used.

Administrators can use this book as a reference when looking over lesson plans, observing classroom instruction and planning meetings as well as professional development sessions. It also provides a common framework for discussion.

When there are staffing decisions to be made, *Boards of Education* can use this handbook to frame and guide questions for potential candidates. It also provides the necessary outline of today's learning standards to serve as a guide in choosing supplemental curriculum materials.

Again, the importance of a ***common framework*** when discussing mathematics in classrooms, buildings, districts, and students' homes **cannot be stressed enough!**

In the event you are unsure about how to proceed in helping your child, keep our credo in mind:

> *"We don't REMEMBER how to DO math, we THINK about how to USE math in order to solve problems."*
> -Christopher Sarlo & Patti J. Dieck

8

GRADE 5- MULTIPLICATION & DIVISION

By meeting the learning standards in this section, fifth grade children will show that they:

Are able to fluently multiply multi-digit whole numbers using the standard algorithm.

Know how to divide whole numbers with up to two-digit divisors, using a variety of strategies.

Fluency with Multiplication

Learning standard 5.NBT.5 says:

Fluently multiply multi-digit whole numbers using the standard algorithm.

What it means:

"Fluent" means "fast and accurate", much the way we expect fluent speakers of a language to choose their words quickly and use them correctly when having conversations. But it doesn't have to mean "from memory". In fifth grade multiplication, it means that children are able to multiply multi-digit numbers, quickly and correctly.

Fifth graders should become **fluent** (fast and accurate - *think* fluent speaker of a language) with the standard algorithm for multiplication. In this case, "fluent" means that students "just know" what to do when faced with two multi-digit numbers that need to be multiplied. They shouldn't need to use a model or place value chart, rather they should be fluent with setting up a multiplication problem vertically, properly aligning all of the place values (ones under ones, tens under tens, hundreds under hundreds, Etc.). Then they should correctly solve it, using all of the conventions of traditional multiplication. These conventions include all of the things most adults remember learning, such as regrouping ("carrying") and placing zeros to "hold" places in the partial products ("place holder zeros").

10

Example:

56 x 72

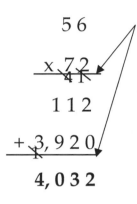

$$
\begin{array}{r}
5\,6 \\
\times\,7\,2 \\
\hline
1\,1\,2 \\
+\,3,9\,2\,0 \\
\hline
4,0\,3\,2
\end{array}
$$

*Notice that in this example, the numbers that were "carried" (the "1" in "12" for example), were placed across the horizontal line separating the problem and the answer. Some children first learned to "carry" this way in second grade when learning to add greater numbers. The slash through the carried numbers signifies that they have been added in...another visual cue for children. If this is what children are familiar with, it makes sense to continue it here.

©2016 Conceptual Learning Associates

Understanding Division

Learning standard 5.NBT.6 says:

Find whole-number quotients of whole numbers with up to four-digit dividends and two-digit divisors, using strategies based on place value, the properties of operations, and/or the relationship between multiplication and division. Illustrate and explain the calculation by using equations, rectangular arrays, and/or area models.

What it means:

The most important idea about division in fifth grade is that even though children will divide up to a four-digit number by a two-digit number, *they are NOT expected to become fluent with the division algorithm until sixth grade.* This means that as fifth graders build on their fourth grade work with division, the focus should be on them truly understanding the process. The methods and strategies that ultimately make the most sense to each individual child are the ones they should use. Children will be exposed to the standard algorithm (the way most adults learned), but for some children it may remain a very abstract idea, and they choose not to use it yet. It's extremely important to keep in mind that, just as was the case with addition and subtraction and multiplication in earlier grades, *not all children will move to using the algorithm at the same time.* This is normal! Children who are NOT pushed too soon to use a single strategy will gain a better understanding of division, and will have more success with the algorithm once they move to using it.

In third and fourth grade children gained an understanding of what the concept of division means: breaking a number or quantity into smaller, equal groups. They also learned to view division as the opposite (inverse) of multiplication, as well as memorized single-digit division facts. In some cases, the focus may have been memorizing multiplication facts in isolation, leading to children having had little exposure to the division facts. A great way to combat this is to use fact triangle cards, or division flash cards for 10 or 15 minutes each day. Children will quickly make the connection and realize that for every multiplication fact they know by heart they already know the corresponding division fact. Learning to associate division with what they already know about multiplication will build a strong foundation for children as they move through fifth grade math…and beyond.

12

In grade 5 children use their multiplication and division facts in order to divide two-, three-, or four-digit numbers by a one- or two-digit number. There are a number of models and strategies that students might be exposed to in order to accomplish this....hopefully they are exposed to all of these:

- Compatible Numbers: A strategy that allows children to estimate before dividing. Children "change" each number in a division problem to a more "friendly" set of numbers in order to get an idea of what the answer will be. For example, to divide 1520 ÷ 72, children would (in their minds) make 1520→1400 and 72→ 70 (because 14 is a multiple of 7). They mentally determine that 1400 ÷ 70 = 20, so children use this quotient (20) as a starting point. They know their actual answer will be near 20.

- Partial Quotients Method: A strategy based on place value that bridges children's work with the area model and place value chart to the long division algorithm. Using the partial quotients method helps children gain an understanding of long division.

- The Standard Algorithm: The method most adults learned for dividing greater numbers (A.K.A. Long Division).

The big idea here is that children gain *an understanding* of how division with greater numbers works. They may not be completely comfortable with standard long division yet and this is OK! The important thing is that they can use a place value strategy to complete the division.

13

Example:

Using Partial Quotients to Divide 1322 ÷ 62

When working with this strategy, each place value is divided separately.

A child using this model knows to begin with the greatest place value first (in this case, the thousands place.) There aren't enough thousands to divide by 62 (there is only 1 thousand), so the child records a partial quotient of zero in the answer area above.

Next, the child divides 13 hundreds by 6. They use their understanding of compatible numbers to reason that "60 x 20 is 1200" and then find that "62 times 20 is 1240", so 20, is recorded in as a partial quotient.

Finally, the child divides 82 ones by 62. They are able to reason that only 1 group of 62 can be made from 82 ones, so 1 is recorded as a partial quotient.

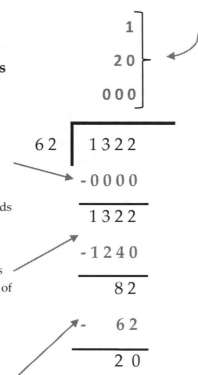

These numbers are placed here as each place value is divided. Because 1322 was divided one place value at a time these numbers are parts of the quotient. To finish the problem these numbers need to be added together.

1322 ÷ 62 = 21 r20

©2016 Conceptual Learning Associates

Example:

Using the Standard Algorithm to Divide 5,969 ÷ 47

```
              127
        ┌──────────
     47 │ 5969
        │-4700  (100 x 47)
          ──────
           1269
        -   940  (20 x 47)
          ──────
            329
        -   329   (7 x 47)
          ──────
              0
```

The child solving this problem used a similar strategy to the one most adults learned. Instead of dividing each individual digit, and then needing to "bring down" the next digits, the division is done by place value. First the 59 hundreds are divided, then the tens, and finally the ones. The entire place value is subtracted each time, instead of just the single digit.

*Many children "get stuck" deciding how many times the divisor (in this case 47) "goes into" each part of the problem.

The child solving this problem used compatible numbers to determine how many groups of 47 could be made at each level of dividing. He or she might have reasoned, "Forty-seven is close to 50, so I can use 50 as a guide. I know that 50 x 100 is 5000. I can multiply by 100." So, 47 is multiplied by 100 and 1 is recorded in the hundreds place of the quotient.

The same strategy is used to divide 1269. 50 x 20 is 1000, so 47 is multiplied by 20 and 2 is recorded in the tens place of the quotient.

To divide 329 the child sees that 329 is close to 350. Since 50 x 7 = 350 the child multiplies 47 x 7 and finds that it is 329. So 7 is recorded in the ones column.

©2016 Conceptual Learning Associates

GRADE 5- PATTERNS & FLUENCY

By meeting the learning standards in this section, fifth grade children will show that they:

Understand that in multi-digit numbers place value increases by ten times as digits move to the left, and are one-tenth as great as digits move to the right.

Can use the standard algorithm to multiply multi-digit whole numbers.

Place Value Chart Patterns

Learning standard 5.NBT.1 says:

Recognize that in a multi-digit number, a digit in one place represents 10 times as much as it represents in the place to its right and 1/10 of what it represents in the place to its left.

What it means:

In fourth grade children studied place value in depth. They learned that each time a number is multiplied by 10 it "shifts" one place to the left (moves from ones to tens, tens to hundreds, hundreds to thousands, Etc.) in the place value chart. When numbers shift left, the ones place is left empty and the open place (in the "ones" column) is filled with a zero. Similarly, when a number is multiplied by 100, two "left shifts" are needed, so two zeros are needed to fill the empty spaces in the ones and tens columns. By working with numbers in this way, children learned that each column in the place value chart is ten times greater than the one to its right.

When most adults learned to multiply numbers by 10, 100, 1000, etc., they were simply taught to "add a zero" (or two, three…etc.) to the original numbers. This is, in effect, what children end up doing, however, we shy away from the phrase "add a zero". That phrase might imply that we are actually adding zero to the original number, which children know wouldn't make sense since adding zero to a number doesn't change it. Teaching the reasoning behind the placement of the zeros at the end of the number is quite helpful to children. Children understand that the zeros are simply filling in spaces left open when the original number shifted.

In fifth grade, children apply this concept to division and decimal numbers less than one. They realize that to shift right, a number is divided by 10. Children are quite comfortable with this idea since they understand the concept of inverse, or opposite, operations. Division is the inverse (opposite) of multiplication, so it makes perfect sense that numbers are divided when they shift to the right instead of multiplied when they shift left. One thousand divided by 10, for example, is one hundred. One hundred divided by 10 is ten. Ten divided by 10 is one. Children continue this pattern to the

17

right side of the decimal point in order to work with decimal numbers. One divided by 10 is one tenth. One tenth divided by 10 is one hundredth, etc.

Example:

This chart shows how a number (in this case 1,000) becomes one-tenth as great each time it shifts to the right. The decimal point separates the whole numbers and the parts of whole numbers, but the pattern is the same from one side of the decimal point to the other.

	$\frac{1}{10}$		$\frac{1}{10}$		$\frac{1}{10}$		$\frac{1}{10}$		$\frac{1}{10}$		$\frac{1}{10}$	

thousands	hundreds	tens	ones	d e c i m a l	tenths	hundredths	thousandths
1	0	0	0	●			
	1	0	0	●			
		1	0	●			
			1	●			
			0	●	1		
			0	●	0	1	
			0	●	0	0	1

©2016 Conceptual Learning Associates

Example:

This chart shows how a number (in this case .001) becomes ten times as great each time it shifts to the left. The decimal point separates the whole numbers and the parts of whole numbers, but the pattern is the same from one side of the decimal point to the other.

X 10   X 10   X 10   X 10   X 10   X 10

thousands	hundreds	tens	ones	d e c i m a l	tenths	hundredths	thousandths
			0	●	0	0	1
			0	●	0	1	
			0	●	1		
			1	●			
		1	0	●			
	1	0	0	●			
1	0	0	0	●			

©2016 Conceptual Learning Associates

Patterns with Multiplication and Division

Learning standard 5.NBT.2 says:

Explain patterns in the number of zeros of the product when multiplying a number by powers of 10, and explain patterns in the placement of the decimal point when a decimal is multiplied or divided by a power of 10. Use whole-number exponents to denote powers of 10.

What it means:

Children first learned to multiply whole numbers by "powers of 10" (10, 100, 1000, etc.) using a place value chart in grade 4. Early in fourth grade they developed the understanding that each column on a place value chart is 10 times greater than the one to its left. Applying this reasoning, children recognized that when any number was multiplied by 10 it becomes 10 times greater so its digits all shift one place to the left in the chart. When all of the digits shift left, the ones place is left empty, and children filled the empty place with a zero, since there were no ones in it. In this way, children came to understand that any number multiplied by 10 must end in a zero, because the ones place will always be left empty after the shift. Since 100 is the same as 10 x 10, multiplying by 100 is the same as multiplying by 10 twice. Any number multiplied by 100 shifts two places to the left, leaving two empty places where zeroes are placed. Children see that any number multiplied by 100 must end in two zeroes.

In fifth grade, children continue with this reasoning. They recognize that whenever a number is multiplied by a power of ten, the number of zeroes in the power of ten tells how many times the number must shift (once for 10, twice for 100, three times for 1,000, etc.) When they are multiplying a whole number by a power of 10, the number of zeroes in the power of 10 also tells how many zeroes need to be placed on the end of the whole number.

Children in fifth grade understand that when they are multiplying a decimal number by a power of 10, they do not automatically add zeroes to show the shifts. Fifth graders know that the places in a place value chart are organized around the decimal point, which separates whole number from parts of numbers. Since children know that the decimal point is stationary (it doesn't move), they are able to see that its position in a number will change when the digits shift.

©2016 Conceptual Learning Associates

Children use what they understand about the inverse (opposite) relationship between multiplication and division in order to apply all of this reasoning to dividing whole numbers and decimals by powers of 10. If numbers increase by 10 times as much as they shift left, then they must decrease by 10 times as they shift right. To divide a number by 10, therefore, means that the number must shift one place to the right. Dividing by 100 shifts a number two places to the right, and so on. Children understand that there is no need to fill the newly empty spaces with zeroes because of their placement at the beginning of the number.

Dividing a number by a power of 10 often results in a decimal number. This is not a problem for fifth grade children. They understand that the decimal point is in a fixed position, to the right of the ones place. When a number that is divided shifts to the right, the decimal point's position within that number will change. The digits will simply shift around it.

Something brand new to fifth graders is using exponents to represent multiplication by a power of 10. Children already understand the relationship between the number of zeroes in the power of 10 and the number of shifts to the left. They use this knowledge to interpret and write multiplication in exponential form. Children interpret 10^3 as "ten multiplied 3 times", which they know is the same as multiplying by 1,000. This enables children to understand the need for writing numbers using exponents. They can see that as numbers become larger it is much more efficient to use exponents. The relationship between the exponent and the number of zeroes in the power of 10 helps children quickly and correctly convert powers of 10 from number form to exponential form and back again.

©2016 Conceptual Learning Associates

Example:

This chart show how a number (in this case .003) shifts to the left as it is multiplied by powers of ten. The equations below the table show the multiplication represented in exponential form.

	thousands	hundreds	tens	ones	tenths	hundredths	thousandths
A					0	0	3
B					0	3	
C					3		
D				3			
E			3	0			
F		3	0	0			
G	3	0	0	0			

A = 0.003 x (zero powers of ten)   or **A = 0.003 x 10^0**

B = 0.003 x 10   or   **B = 0.003 x 10^1**

C = 0.003 x 100   or   **C = 0.003 x 10^2**

D = 0.003 x 1,000   or   **D = 0.003 x 10^3**

E = 0.003 x 10,000   or   **E = 0.003 x 10^4**

F = 0.003 x 100,000   or   **F = 0.003 x 10^5**

G = 0.003 x 1,000,000   or   **G = 0.003 x 10^6**

©2016 Conceptual Learning Associates

Example:

This chart show how a number (in this case 3,000) shifts to the right as it is divided by powers of ten. The equations below the table show the division represented in exponential form.

	thousands	hundreds	tens	ones	tenths	hundredths	thousandths
A	3	0	0	0			
B		3	0	0			
C			3	0			
D				3			
E					3		
F					0	3	
G					0	0	3

$A = 3{,}000 \div$ zero powers of ten   or $A = 3{,}000 \div 10^0$

$B = 3{,}000 \div 10$ or $B = 3{,}000 \div 10^1$

$C = 3{,}000 \div 100$ or $C = 3{,}000 \div 10^2$

$D = 3{,}000 \div 1{,}000$ or $D = 3{,}000 \div 10^3$

$E = 3{,}000 \div 10{,}000$ or $E = 3{,}000 \div 10^4$

$F = 3{,}000 \div 100{,}000$ or $F = 3{,}000 \div 10^5$

$G = 3{,}000 \div 1{,}000{,}000$ or $G = 3{,}000 \div 10^6$

23

©2016 Conceptual Learning Associates

Fluency with Multiplication

Learning standard 5.NBT.5 says:

Fluently multiply multi-digit whole numbers using the standard algorithm.

What it means:

Fifth graders should become **fluent** (fast and accurate - *think* fluent speaker of a language) with the standard algorithm for multiplication when working with whole numbers. But this certainly doesn't have to mean "from memory". In this case, "fluent" means that students "just know" what to do when faced with two multi-digit whole numbers that need to be multiplied. They shouldn't need to use an area model or place value chart; rather they should be fluent with setting up a multiplication problem vertically, while properly aligning all of the place values (ones under ones, tens under tens, hundreds under hundreds, etc.) Then they should correctly solve the problem, using all of the conventions of traditional multiplication. This is includes the idea of remembering to use zeros to "hold" place value columns as needed (when multiplying by tens, hundreds, etc.).

Example:

375 x 293

```
        3 7 5

    x   2 9 3
          2 1
      1 1 2 5
          6 4
      3 3 7 5 0        Children know that they need to place a zero here because they
          1 1          are multiplying by 90 at this level, not simply by 9.
    + 7 5 0 0 0        Here they know that they need to place two zeros because they
                       are multiplying by 200 at this level, not simply by 2.
    1 0 9, 8 7 5
```

©2016 Conceptual Learning Associates

* In the problem on the previous page, the "carrying" is done between each level instead of all at the top. This allows students to more easily see which numbers they have already worked with. This is not "the right way" or the only way to use the multiplication algorithm, nor is it "wrong". Children are free to use the algorithm in whichever way works best for them. The important thing is that children become fluent using one strategy consistently.

25

GRADE 5-DECIMALS

By meeting the learning standards in this section, fifth grade children will show that they:

Can read and write decimal numbers using numbers, word and expanded form.

Are able to compare two decimal numbers and record the comparison using <, >, or =.

Understand how to use place value to round decimal numbers to any place.

Can add, subtract, multiply and divide decimal numbers (to the hundredths place)

Compare Decimals

Learning standard 5.NBT.3 says:

Read and write decimals to thousandths using base-ten numerals, number names, and expanded form, e.g., 347.392 = 3 × 100 + 4 × 10 + 7 × 1 + 3 × (1/10) + 9 × (1/100) + 2 × (1/1000)
Compare two decimals to thousandths based on meanings of the digits in each place, using >, =, and < symbols to record the results of comparisons.

What it means:

In grade 4 children worked with reading and writing whole numbers using numerals (often called "standard form"), number names ("word form") and expanded form (where each digit's place value is written out completely.) In grade 5 they apply this work to reading and writing decimal numbers in all three forms. Understanding these different forms helps children compare the value of two different decimal numbers.

Place value strategies are very helpful when fifth graders are comparing decimal numbers. They may use a place value chart or write each number in its expanded form. The results of the comparisons are recorded by writing number sentences that contain <, >, and = symbols. (Most often children are asked to fill in the blank between two numbers with one of the comparison symbols.)

The numbers children are asked to compare in grade 5 may be presented in different forms. They may, for example, be asked to compare one number written in *standard form* to another written in *word form*. In cases like this, children should be encouraged to rewrite one of the numbers so that it is in the same form as the other one. (Placing each number in a place value chart is a helpful strategy for some children, enabling them to more easily see which of the two numbers is greater.)

Decimal numbers are often confusing for children because sometimes a "shorter" number, like 0.9, is greater than a "longer" number, like 0.63. The simplest way for children to "see" how the digits within two different numbers relate to each other is seeing them inside of a place value chart. Eventually, children will be able to visualize this mentally, using what they know about expanded form, no longer needing to create the chart. The important thing is for children to rely on *place value understanding* when

27

determining the relative values of numbers. Some children will move away from the chart more quickly than others…this is OK!

©2016 Conceptual Learning Associates

Example:

Compare using <, >, or =.

73.9 ◯ 73.901

A child solving this problem might create a place value table and put both numbers into it in order to see how they line up, and determine which is greater.

hundreds	tens	ones		tenths	hundredths	thousandths
	7	3	.	9		
	7	3	.	9	0	1

Once the numbers are lined up, it is easy for him or her to see that 73.901 is the greater number.

73.9 ⟨ < ⟩ 73.901

Another child might visualize or write out the expanded forms of each number.

$$(7 \times 10) + (3 \times 1) + (9 \times \frac{1}{10})$$

$$(7 \times 10) + (3 \times 1) + (9 \times \frac{1}{10}) + (1 \times \frac{1}{1000}) \leftarrow$$

73.9 ⟨ < ⟩ 73.901

When the two numbers are compared place by place in expanded form children see this number is greater because it has one thousandth more than the other number.

29

Example:
Compare using <, >, or =.

673.994 ◯ 673.995

hundreds	tens	ones		tenths	hundredths	thousandths
6	7	3	•	9	9	4
6	7	3	•	9	9	5

After placing both numbers in the place value chart, a child solving this problem thinks, "All of the digits in the whole number places are the same. So are the tenths and hundredths of the numbers. But the thousandths place digits are different. Four is less than five, so 673.994 is less than 673.995"

673.994 (<) 673.995

Or

$$(6 \times 100) + (7 \times 10) + (3 \times 1) + (9 \times \frac{1}{10}) + (9 \times \frac{1}{100}) + (4 \times \frac{1}{1000})$$

$$(6 \times 100) + (7 \times 10) + (3 \times 1) + (9 \times \frac{1}{10}) + (9 \times \frac{1}{100}) + (5 \times \frac{1}{1000})$$

When the two numbers are compared place by place in expanded form children see this number is greater because it has a greater digit in the thousandths place.

673.994 (<) 673.995

©2016 Conceptual Learning Associates

Example:
Compare using <, >, or =.

295.01 ◯ 295.001

hundreds	tens	ones		tenths	hundredths	thousandths
2	9	5	•	0	1	
2	9	5	•	0	0	1

295.01 (>) 295.001

Or

$(2 \times 100) + (9 \times 10) + (5 \times 1) + (1 \times \frac{1}{100})$ ⬅ *When the two numbers are compared place by place in expanded form children see this number is greater because it has a greater digit in the hundredths place.*

$(2 \times 100) + (9 \times 10) + (5 \times 1) + (1 \times \frac{1}{1000})$

295.01 (>) 295.001

31

Example:

Compare using <, >, or =.

35.9 ◯ **thirty five and twenty-seven hundredths**

hundreds	tens	ones		tenths	hundredths	thousandths
	3	5	•	9		
	3	5	•	2	7	

35.9 (>) 35.27

Or

$(3 \times 10) + (5 \times 1) + (9 \times \frac{1}{10})$ ⬅ *When the two numbers are compared place by place in expanded form children see this number is greater because it has a greater digit in the hundredths place.*

$(3 \times 10) + (5 \times 1) + (2 \times \frac{1}{10}) + (7 \times \frac{1}{100})$

35.9 (>) 35.27

*A very common error when comparing decimal numbers is thinking that the number containing the greater number of digits (the "longer" one) is the greater number. Here, 35.27 appears greater than 35.9 to some children because with whole numbers 27 is indeed greater than 9. Writing both numbers in a place value chart helps children see and correct this mistake.

©2016 Conceptual Learning Associates

Rounding Decimals

Learning standard 5.NBT.4 says:

Use place value understanding to round decimals to any place.

What it means:

Fifth graders round decimal numbers containing multiple digits to any place value. This means they are given a number and asked to round it to a specified place. To do this, they may use whichever strategy works best for them. Similar to when they compared numbers, children may start out using one model, and eventually move away from it as they become more proficient at "seeing it" mentally.

The big (and important!) idea here is that children should NOT be taught a series of "rounding steps". Teaching "rounding steps" keeps rounding an isolated skill, not connected to other areas of math. It is much too easy to forget "how to round", when it is not taught from a place of meaning.

The way children in fifth grade are taught rounding is directly related to their understanding of place value. The number line is the most effective model for children to actually SEE which number the one being rounded is closest to. Children have been working with the number line since kindergarten and thoroughly understand how it works, making it a familiar and "comfortable" model for teaching rounding. To round using a number line children should look at the digit in the place they are asked to round to, and then imagine which of those units the number would be closest to on a number line.

> *For example, **to round 2.738 to the nearest hundredth** children first determine that there are 273 hundredths in this number (easily seen in a place value chart.) When picturing 2.738 on a number line, children recognize that it would fall between 273 hundredths (2.73) and 274 hundredths (2.74). Finally, children simply decide which group of hundredths 2.738 is closer to. In this case, it is closer to 274 hundredths. So 2.738 rounded to the nearest hundredth is 2.74.*

Eventually, children will be able to visualize this mentally, no longer needing to create a place value chart or number line. The important thing is for children to rely on *place value understanding* when rounding numbers. Some children will move away from the models more quickly than others...this is OK!

©2016 Conceptual Learning Associates

Example:

Name the underlined place. Round to the underlined place.

0.362

hundreds	tens	ones		tenths	hundredths	thousandths
		0	•	3	6	2

(A vertical number line is often helpful for children to mentally "see" the numbers increasing from bottom to top. This could be replaced with a horizontal line if it is more familiar.)

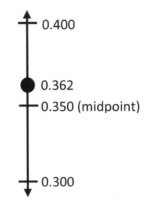

Children first determine that the underlined place is the tenths place.

The number line they create reflects the "tenths" that 0.362 falls between. Since 0.362 is greater than 3 tenths but less than 4 tenths, those are the endpoints on the number line.

0.350 is the midpoint between 0.300 (or 3 tenths) and 0.400 (or 4 tenths). 0.362 is greater than the midpoint, therefore it is "closer" on a number line to 0.400 than 0.300.

So…

0.362 rounded to the nearest tenth is 0.4.

*Some children may prefer to write this answer as .400. This is OK! It may help children "see" the connection to the rounding of whole numbers that they already know how to do if they read the answer as "Three hundred, sixty-two thousandths rounds to four hundred thousandths."

34

©2016 Conceptual Learning Associates

Example:

Name the underlined place. Round to the underlined place.

0.3<u>4</u>2

hundreds	tens	ones		tenths	hundredths	thousandths
		0	•	3	4	2

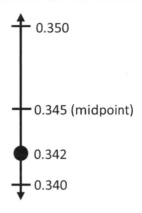

(A vertical number line is often helpful for children to mentally "see" the numbers increasing from bottom to top. This could be replaced with a horizontal line if it is more familiar.)

The 4 is in the hundredths place therefore our number line reflects the "hundredths" that 0.342 falls between (0.342 is greater than 0.34 and less than 0.35).

0.345 is the midpoint between 0.340 (34 hundredths) and 0.350 (35 hundredths). 0.342 is less than the midpoint, therefore it is "closer" on a number line to 0.340 than 0.350.

So…

0.342 rounded to the nearest hundredth is 0.34.

*Some children may prefer to write this answer as .340. This is OK! It may help children "see" the connection to the rounding of whole numbers that they already know how to do if they read the answer as "Three hundred, forty-two thousandths rounds to three hundred, forty thousandths."

©2016 Conceptual Learning Associates

Decimal Operations

Learning standard 5.NF.7 says:

Add, subtract, multiply, and divide decimals to hundredths, using concrete models or drawings and strategies based on place value, properties of operations, and/or the relationship between addition and subtraction; relate the strategy to a written method and explain the reasoning used.

What it means:

By the end of fourth grade, children were required to fluently add and subtract whole numbers up to 1 million using a standard algorithm. Being "fluent" with math operations means knowing how to set up and complete the operations quickly and accurately, without needing to stop and think about what comes next (much like we expect someone who fluently speaks a language to speak quickly and accurately without needing to stop and think about what comes next.) Part of "fluently" adding and subtracting whole numbers with up to 7 digits is understanding how the digits of each number should be placed in the problem when the numbers are stacked vertically. When the numbers contain different amounts of digits, children who are fluent will automatically line up the correct place (values) of each number (ones with ones, tens with tens, hundreds with hundreds, etc.) In fifth grade children build on this understanding to add and subtract decimal numbers.

Using place value to line up digits helps fifth grade children set up decimal addition and subtraction problems correctly. It is natural for children first working with decimal numbers to want to line them up "to the right" regardless of how many digits are in each number…this is often the thinking before children realize that lining whole numbers up "to the right" IS lining them up by place value places. This misconception is the biggest hurdle fifth graders need to get over when working with decimals. The more children understand about place value, and the more practice they have working with decimal numbers, the more success they will have.

The important thing for children to remember is that everything they know to be true about working with whole numbers is true for working with decimal numbers. They can still use the commutative property (changing the order of the numbers being added) when adding, since some children will prefer to write problems such that the number

©2016 Conceptual Learning Associates

with more digits is on top of the one with less digits. When subtracting, however, children must remember that, just as with whole numbers, the order of the numbers in the problem cannot be changed. This is an important concept since sometimes a decimal number with a greater value will appear "smaller" than another number, even though it isn't. This sometimes entices children to switch the order of the numbers because the problem "looks better" that way.

One strategy that often helps children correctly line up decimal numbers before adding or subtracting them is the use of zeroes to *hold* place value places open. Children know that placing zeroes in front of any whole number, or at the end of any decimal number will not change the value of the number. Using these zeroes to fill "open" places can often make numbers "look the same" as they will then have the same number of digits.

Another helpful strategy is for children to remember that any whole number can be written as a decimal number simply by showing it with a decimal point and a zero. The value of the whole number doesn't change...it is just being represented as a certain number of "wholes" and zero "parts". Practice helps children to correctly line up numbers, especially when a decimal is being subtracted from a whole number.

37

Example:

Find the sum of 37.9 and 152.31.

To solve, this child first used the commutative property to switch the order of the numbers. 152.31 contains more digits, so it might "feel" more comfortable for children to see it set up this way (although it is not necessary as long as children line up tens with tens, ones with ones and tenths with tenths etc.):

$$
\begin{array}{r}
152.31 \\
+\ \ 37.90 \\
\hline
190.21
\end{array}
$$

Next, this child placed a zero in the hundredths place of 37.9, knowing that this would not change the numbers value, but making it line up evenly on the right side…which is very comfortable for fifth graders.

©2016 Conceptual Learning Associates

Example:

Find the difference between 143 and 32.186.

To solve, this child first placed a decimal point and three zeroes (in the tenths, hundredths and thousandths places of 143.) This didn't change the value of 143, but it gave the child real digits above the 1 and the 8 in 32.186 to subtract from once the problem was set up:

$$
\begin{array}{r}
\overset{2\;\;\;9\;\;\;9\;\;\;10}{14\boxed{3.000}} \\
-\quad 32.186 \\
\hline
110.814
\end{array}
$$

*Notice that with five digits 32.186 might initially "Look" greater than 143 which only has three digits. Lining up by place value places allows children to see that they should place the decimal point and three zeroes into the problem.

Whenever children add or subtract decimal numbers, they must remember to include the decimal point in their answer. For most children this just makes sense…in fact it wouldn't make sense not to! (It's important to use this reasoning when reminding children to include the decimal point in their answers, rather than teaching them the "final step" of "bringing down" the decimal point. Remember, "Steps" don't stick, but reasoning does.)

*When determining "where the decimal is" in the answer children can look only at the whole numbers and estimate (in this case the difference). 140 – 30 = 110 so the decimal point should be placed in 110814 so that it will be approximately equal to 110.

110.814

39

©2016 Conceptual Learning Associates

Multiplication

Thinking of a decimal as a *"unit"* is incredibly useful as children first begin to multiply decimal numbers. It helps them see that everything they understand to be true about multiplying whole numbers is true for multiplying decimals. Reading the number as a set of units, such as "tenths" or "hundredths" is helpful.

Example:

Find the product of 4 and 0.6.

4 x 0.6 = ?

Read as *"4 times 6 tenths"*

The thinking is simply "4 times 6" with a *"unit"* of tenths.

If the unit were "puppies", then

4 times 6 puppies would have a product of 24 puppies.

4 x 6 (puppies) is 24 (puppies)

4 x 6 (puppies) = 24 puppies

So....

4 x 6(tenths) is 24(tenths).

4 x 6(tenths) = 24 tenths

It is perfectly acceptable for children to write the product as

"24 tenths", or to use place value reasoning to write it as "2.4".

40

©2016 Conceptual Learning Associates

4 x 0.06

Read as *"4 times 6 hundredths"*

The thinking is simply "4 times 6" with a *"unit"* of hundredths.

So 4 x 6(hundredths) is 24(hundredths).

4 x 6(hundredths) = 24 hundredths

It is perfectly acceptable for children to write the product as either "24 hundredths", or "0.24".

In the next examples, area models are used to multiply. Some of the models show rectangles divided almost evenly. Others are broken into "relatively proportional" size parts (greater numbers are represented by larger sections). When children first use the area model, their models may appear more evenly divided. This will change as they develop deeper understanding of how the model represents the problem. Children should be guided toward creating more proportionally sized parts, as this gives them another "visual" cue. It makes sense that larger-size parts will contain greater partial products. Children can rely on this when determining if their answers are reasonable.

41

©2016 Conceptual Learning Associates

Example:

A 2-digit number times a 1-digit decimal number

Here a child uses an area model to decompose (break apart) the two digit number before multiplying each part by the decimal number. This results in two "partial answers", called *partial products*. These partial products are added together to find the final total.

Once again, "units" (in this case *tenths*) are shown, as this thinking is also appropriate. It isn't necessary to include all of the notations shown in the model below. Sometimes children will use the decimal number, sometimes they will use the unit representation. Either is fine…children should use the notations that make the most sense to them.

24 x 0.6

(Read as "24 times 6 tenths")

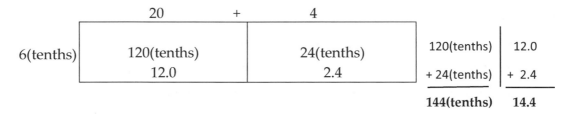

24 x 6(tenths) = 144 tenths

Or

24 x 0.6 = 14.4

©2016 Conceptual Learning Associates

Example:

A 3-digit number with a decimal times a 1-digit number

3.24 x 6

	2(tenths) + 4 (hundredths)	
3.0 +	0.2 +	0.04

18 18.00	12 (tenths) 1.2	24 (hundredths) 0.24

6

```
18                      18.00
12(tenths)               1.2
+ 24(hundredths)       + 0.24
                       --------
1944(hundredths)        19.44
```

324(hundredths) x 6 = 1944(hundredths)

3.24 x 6 = 19.44

This model shows both decimal number and unit notations for each value. Children don't need to include all of this when they use this model, they should use the one that makes the most sense to them.

_____

The same "unit" thinking applies without the model:

3.24 x 6 = ?

3 and 24 hundredths OR *324 hundredths* times *6*

324(hundredths) x 6 = ?

324(hundredths) x 6 = 1944(hundredths)

3.24 x 6 = 19.44

©2016 Conceptual Learning Associates

Example:

A 2-digit decimal number times a 1-digit decimal number

Children are familiar with multiplying powers of ten:

ten x ten = hundred, ten x hundred = thousand, ten x thousand = ten thousand.

The same thinking applies here as children multiply decimal numbers:

Tenth x tenth = hundredth, tenth x hundredth = thousandth, etc.

2.4 x 0.8

24 tenths x 8 tenths

	4(tenths)			
	2.0	+	0.4	
8(tenths)	16(tenths) 1.6		32(hundredths) 0.32	16 (tenths) 1.6
0.8				+ 32 (hundredths) + 0.32
				192(hundredths) **1.92**

The same "unit" thinking applies without the model:

2.4 x 0.8 = ?

24 tenths times 8 tenths

24(tenths) x 8(tenths) = ?

24(tenths) x 8(tenths) = 192(hundredths)

2.4 x 0.8 = 1.92

©2016 Conceptual Learning Associates

Example:

A 2-digit decimal number times a 2-digit decimal number

5.6 x 7.2

56 tenths x 72 tenths

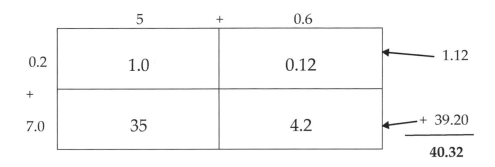

56 tenths x 72 tenths = 4032 hundredths

5.6 x 7.2 = 40.32

The same "unit" thinking applies without the model:

5.6 x 7.2 = ?

56 tenths times *72 tenths*

56(tenths) x 72(tenths) = ?

56(tenths) x 72(tenths) = 4032(hundredths)

5.6 x 7.2 = 40.32

45

©2016 Conceptual Learning Associates

When solving problems like the one in the previous example, some children may notice that this type of problem is very similar to what they already know about two-digit by two-digit multiplication. They may see that multiplying 5.6 x 7.2 is a lot like multiplying 56 x 72... especially when they are using unit thinking. For most adults, this thinking makes a lot of sense. When most of us learned decimal multiplication we were taught to "ignore the decimal points, do the multiplication, and then place the decimal into the answer." This is essentially what we are still doing. Unit thinking allows children to "ignore the decimal point and multiply" but with a reason for doing so...using units helps them keep the value of each number in mind while working. After multiplying, children are able to correctly place the decimal point into their answer using reasoning. In the example above, for example, tenths are being multiplied by tenths, so the answer must be expressed in hundredths, which tells the child that the decimal point in the answer must be placed so that the answer represents hundredths.

Eventually children become comfortable moving away from models for multiplication. The first step in this move is often to a strategy called "partial products". Children were first introduced to this "bridge" strategy (meaning that it "bridges" children from the model to the algorithm.) in grade 4.

©2016 Conceptual Learning Associates

Example:

Partial Products Strategy for Multiplication

To solve this problem without a model, a fifth grader might choose to use the partial products strategy. When setting it up, he or she might think, "I can use what I know about the area model to set up a partial products problem. I just have to use expanded form to take apart 3.24. Then I can multiply each part by 6."

$$3.24 \times 6 =$$

$$3.0 + 0.2 + 0.04$$

X	6

24 hundredths	0.24
12 tenths	1.20
+ 18 ones	+ 18.00
1,944 hundredths	19.44

After multiplying each of the parts, the child thinks, "Since I multiplied each of the parts of 3.24 separately, adding the parts together will give me the whole product."

©2016 Conceptual Learning Associates

Examples:
Partial Products for Decimal Multiplication

2.4 x 0.8 =

2.0 + 0.4
X____0.8
32 hundredths   0.32
+____16 tenths____   + 1.60
192 hundredths   1.92

5.6 x 7.2 =

5.0 + 0.6
X 7.0 + 0.2
12 hundredths   0.12
1 one   1.00
42 tenths   4.2
+ 35 ones____   35.00
4,032 hundredths   40.32

Children were first exposed to the standard algorithm in fourth grade, when they multiplied multi-digit whole numbers. In fifth grade children expand on what they know by multiplying decimal numbers with the algorithm. By the time children in fifth grade are ready to use the standard algorithm for multiplying decimal numbers they will have built a foundation of understanding that will make using the algorithm simple.   Rather than "remembering the steps" of multiplying, children multiply in an order that feels natural and makes sense.

©2016 Conceptual Learning Associates

Examples:

3.24 x 6 =

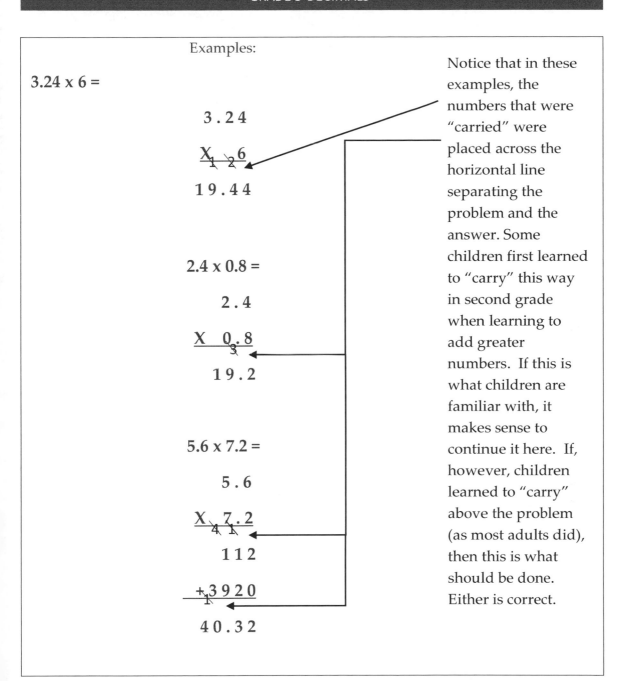

3 . 2 4

X 1 2 6

1 9 . 4 4

Notice that in these examples, the numbers that were "carried" were placed across the horizontal line separating the problem and the answer. Some children first learned to "carry" this way in second grade when learning to add greater numbers. If this is what children are familiar with, it makes sense to continue it here. If, however, children learned to "carry" above the problem (as most adults did), then this is what should be done. Either is correct.

2.4 x 0.8 =

2 . 4

X   0 . 8
        3

1 9 . 2

5.6 x 7.2 =

5 . 6

X   7 . 2
    4   1

1 1 2

+ 3 9 2 0
  1

4 0 . 3 2

©2016 Conceptual Learning Associates

<u>Division</u>

In grade 5 children use multiplication and division facts, and their deep understanding of what multiplication and division mean, in order to divide decimal numbers. There are a number of models and strategies that students might be exposed to in order to accomplish this…and they will likely include:

- Place Value Chart (A model that is very familiar to children, and when used for division, allows them to see how a multi-digit decimal number should be divided from the greatest to the least place value.)
- Partial Quotients Method (A model that bridges children's work with the place value chart to the algorithm.)
- The Standard Algorithm (The method most adults learned for multiplying decimal numbers.)

The big idea here is that children gain *an understanding* of how division with decimal numbers works. They may not be completely comfortable with the standard long division algorithm yet and this is OK! (Fluency with the division algorithm happens in sixth grade.) The important thing is that children can use a place value strategy to complete the division.

*On the next 7 pages, the same two problems are solved repeatedly to show the progression of strategies children might use, beginning with drawing circles in a place value chart and progressing to the use of the standard algorithm. Important to remember is that fifth grade children do not yet need to be fluent with the use of the division algorithm; this is a sixth grade standard. The important thing is that fifth graders understand what is happening when one number is divided by another.

©2016 Conceptual Learning Associates

Example:

1.24 ÷ 4 =

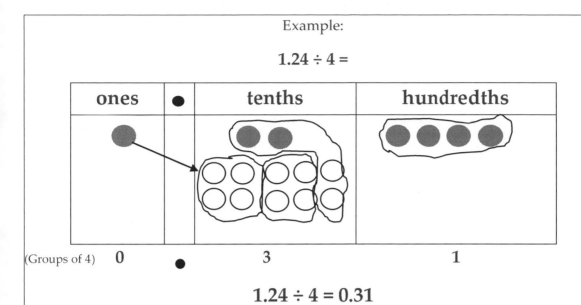

(Groups of 4)   0   •   3   1

1.24 ÷ 4 = 0.31

To solve this problem a child first draws a place value chart and places the appropriate number of circles in each section (shown here as the closed circles.) Since children are familiar with the idea that division creates equal-size groups, the child begins with the greatest place value and circles groups of 4 (since we're dividing by 4.)

There aren't enough ones to create a group of 4, so the one is shifted to the tenths column, becoming 10 tenths (shown here as the open circles.) Once again, the child looks for groups of 4 circles, and is able to circle 3 groups.

There are no "leftover" tens (that could not be grouped) so the hundredths column is divided next. In the hundredths column the child is able to circle 1 group of 4 circles. Since there are no "leftover" hundredths, the child is finished dividing.

So, 1.24 divided by 4 equals 0.31. This answer is reasonable because 1.24 (a little more than 1) is being divided by 4, which is a greater number. Children know that 1 divided by 4 is one fourth, or 0.25, so since the starting number was a little more than 1, the quotient will be a little more than 0.25.

51

Example:

$$17.76 \div 16 =$$

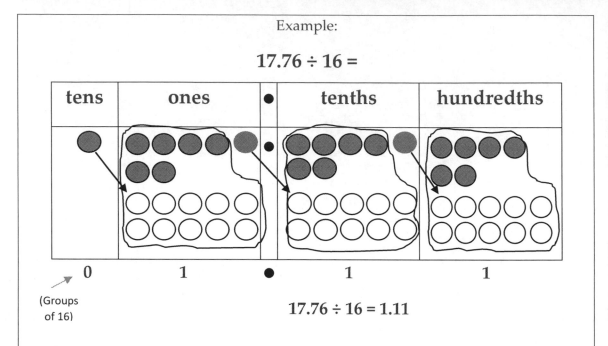

(Groups of 16)

$$17.76 \div 16 = 1.11$$

To solve this problem a child first draws a place value chart and places the appropriate number of circles in each section (shown here as the closed circles.) Since children are familiar with the idea that division creates equal-size groups, the child begins with the greatest place value and circles groups of 16 (since we're dividing by 16.)

There aren't enough tens to create a group of 16, so the ten is shifted to the ones column, becoming 10 ones (shown here as the open circles.) Once again, the child looks for groups of 16 circles, and is able to circle 1 group. The "leftover" one is shifted to the right and becomes 10 tenths. The child continues dividing each place value column, moving "leftovers" as needed, until the problem is solved.

Children can see that the answer of 1.11 is reasonable by looking at the whole numbers. 17 divided by 16 would equal a little more than 1...which is what the correct quotient ended up being.

©2016 Conceptual Learning Associates

$$1.24 \div 4 =$$

ones	•	tenths	hundredths
1		2	4
		12	
		$12 \div 4 = 3$	$4 \div 4 = 1$

(Groups of 4)   0   •   3   1

$$1.24 \div 4 = 0.31$$

*In these examples, digits replace the circles in the previous example. This is a natural progression for children as drawing the circles becomes cumbersome. (To help you "see" this transition, the problem below is the same as the one on the previous page.)

$$17.76 \div 16 =$$

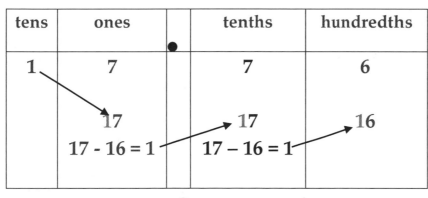

tens	ones	•	tenths	hundredths
1	7		7	6
	17		17	16
	$17 - 16 = 1$		$17 - 16 = 1$	

(Groups of 16)   0   1   •   1   1

$$17.76 \div 16 = 1.11$$

53

©2016 Conceptual Learning Associates

Example:

$$1.24 \div 4 =$$

When working with this strategy, each place value is divided separately.

A child using this model knows to begin with the greatest place value first (in this case, the tens place.) There aren't enough ones to divide by 4, so the child records a partial quotient of zero.

Next, the child divides 12 tenths by 4. They know that "4 times 3 tenths is 12 tenths", so .3 is recorded in as a partial quotient. It is recorded as .30 so that all parts of the quotient are expressed to the same place value as the dividend. (Remember placing zeros to the right of the last digit in a decimal number doesn't change the number's value.)

Finally, the child divides 4 hundredths by 4. Since 4 times 1 hundredth is 4 hundredths, 0.01 is recorded as a partial quotient.

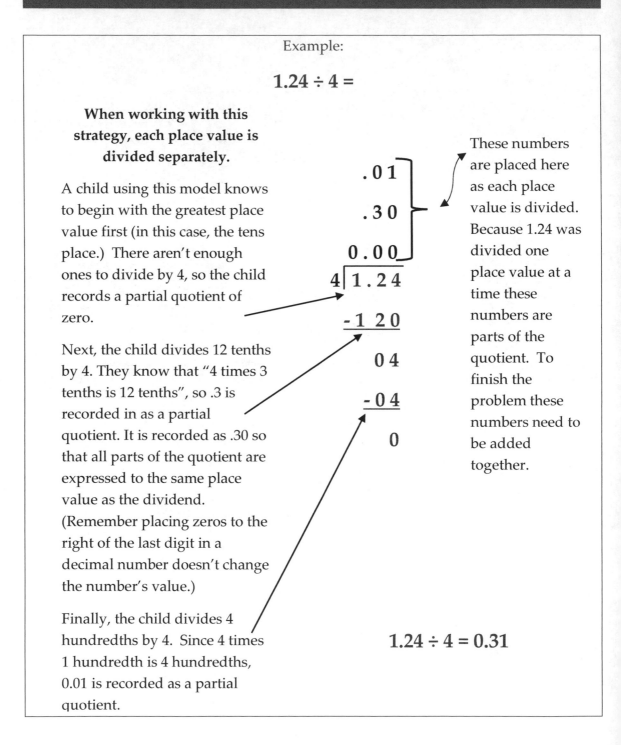

These numbers are placed here as each place value is divided. Because 1.24 was divided one place value at a time these numbers are parts of the quotient. To finish the problem these numbers need to be added together.

$$1.24 \div 4 = 0.31$$

©2016 Conceptual Learning Associates

Example:

$$17.76 \div 16 =$$

$$
\begin{array}{r}
.01 \\
.10 \\
1.00 \\
00.00 \\
\end{array}
\Big\}
\longrightarrow
\begin{array}{r}
.01 \\
.10 \\
1.00 \\
+00.00 \\
\hline
1.11 \\
\end{array}
$$

$$16\overline{)17.76}$$

$$-16\ 00$$

$$1\ \ 76$$

$$-\ 1\ \ 6\ 0 \text{ (tenths)}$$

$$1\ 6$$

$$-\ 1\ 6 \text{ (hundredths)}$$

$$0$$

$$17.76 \div 16 = 1.11$$

©2016 Conceptual Learning Associates

Example:

$$1.24 \div 4 =$$

1 one divided by 4 is 0.

12 hundredths divided by 4 is 30 hundredths. 4 x 30 hundredths = 12 hundredths.

Finally 4 hundredths divided by 4 is 1 hundredth.

```
      0 . 3 1
  4 | 1 . 2 4
    - 1   2 0
          4
    -     4
          0
```

The child solving this problem used a similar strategy to the one most adults learned. Instead of dividing each individual digit, and then needing to "bring down" the next digit, the division is done by place value. First the ones are divided, then the tenths, and finally the hundredths. The entire place value is subtracted each time, instead of just the single digit.

1 one divided by 4 is 0.

12 tenths divided by 4 is 3 tenths. 4 x 3 tenths = 12 tenths.

Finally 4 hundredths divided by 4 is 1 hundredth.

```
      0 . 3 1
  4 | 1 . 2 4
    - 1   2
      0 4
    - 0 4
        0
```

The child solving this problem used the same strategy most adults learned. Each individual digit is divided and then the next digit to the right is "brought down" so the division can continue.

$$1.24 \div 4 = 0.31$$

©2016 Conceptual Learning Associates

$$17.76 \div 16 =$$

```
      0 1 . 1 1
16 ) 1 7 . 7 6
   - 1 6
       1   7
   -   1   6
             1   6
   -         1   6
                 0
```

$$17.76 \div 16 = 1.11$$

©2016 Conceptual Learning Associates

GRADE 5- FRACTIONS

By meeting the learning standards in this section, fifth grade children will show that they:

Are able to add and subtract fractions with different denominators.

Use addition and subtraction of fractions to solve word problems.

Understand that a fraction can be interpreted as a division problem (the numerator divided by the denominator).

Know how to multiply fractions and mixed numbers.

Recognize that multiplying by a fraction less than one results in a number less than the starting number; multiplying by a fraction greater than one results in a number greater than the original number.

Know how to divide a whole number by a fraction.

Use fraction multiplication and division to solve word problems.

Important Information about 5th-Grade Fraction Work

It will most likely not surprise a single fifth grade parent to learn that the fraction work fifth graders do looks and feels very different from fractions the way we learned them. While this fact is true for much of the work done in grade 5, fractions somehow look even a little "more different". Maybe this is because fractions have traditionally been a tricky topic. Most adults who remember being uncomfortable with math as a child report that fractions was the area which gave them the most trouble.

With all of that in mind, the following points are included here to help you better understand the work you will see throughout this section.

- Fractions "act" like any other numbers. The big difference between fractions and whole numbers is that fractions have two parts. Children understand that the bottom number in a fraction is simply the "unit" that is represented by the top number. So just like $3 = 1 + 1 + 1$, $\frac{3}{4} = \frac{1}{4} + \frac{1}{4} + \frac{1}{4}$. (The 4 in the bottom of the fraction simply tells us that our unit is "fourths", or the whole has been broken into four equal parts.) Once they understand this simple concept, children are able to work with any fractions.

- All fraction work can be done horizontally. Yes, we mean from left to right. Children may have seen this in grade 4. Stacking fractions sometimes causes confusion and makes it difficult for children to keep track of what they do when solving problems. Throughout this section, the examples that follow each standard will reflect both horizontal and vertical fraction work. Within each example we have included explanations and arrows to show exactly how it works. Children should be encouraged to work either horizontally or vertically depending on what they are used to.

- When most adults were first introduced to fractions, we learned that whenever "the top number was larger than the bottom number the fraction was called IMPROPER". The term "improper fraction" is no longer widely used. The

©2016 Conceptual Learning Associates

reason for this is simple: It IS possible to have more than 2 halves, or four fourths, etc. Simply having a greater number in the numerator of a fraction doesn't mean there is something "wrong" , as the term "improper" might imply. While some still use the term "improper fraction", many textbook series refer to these fractions as "fractions greater than one". This is also what we've done in this book. Some teachers, and possibly even a few publishers, will still refer to these fractions greater than one as improper. This is OK. The important thing is that you and your child are aware that these terms are interchangeable.

- One last thing that today's adults were taught about fractions is that they must always be "reduced", "simplified" or expressed in "lowest terms". Once again, this is something you will be seeing less and less of. While it is important for children to understand that fractions having equal values can be written using different numbers, it is NOT always necessary for a fraction to be expressed in its lowest terms. A child relating four inches to one foot, for example, is perfectly correct to state that four inches is $\frac{4}{12}$ of a foot. It is not necessary to express it as $\frac{1}{3}$. Doing so might even be confusing for some students. Some teachers, and possibly even a few publishers, might still teach this skill to students. This is OK. The important thing is that children let the context of a situation dictate when they will and will not simplify (reduce) a fraction.

- A lot of what is shown and explained in this section builds directly from work students did in fourth grade. For those struggling to make sense of some things, or just not "getting it", it may be helpful to read through the fractions section of the grade 4 book from this series (this is when children are first introduced to fractions).

©2016 Conceptual Learning Associates

Add and Subtract Fractions

Learning standard 5.NF.1 says:

Add and subtract fractions with unlike denominators (including mixed numbers) by replacing given fractions with equivalent fractions in such a way as to produce an equivalent sum or difference of fractions with like denominators. For example, 2/3 + 5/4 = 8/12 + 15/12 = 23/12. (In general, a/b + c/d = (ad + bc)/bd.)

What it means:

In fourth grade children developed the understanding that the denominator of a fraction is a "label" of sorts…it names the number of pieces that the whole quantity was divided into. Since the denominator is a label, children know that it makes no sense to change the denominator when adding (or subtracting.) This, however, is only true when children are adding or subtracting equal parts of the same size wholes (halves plus halves, sixths minus sixths, etc.)

In fifth grade, children are exposed to working with different size parts of the same size wholes. Now, they add and subtract different size fractions. To do this, they need to be familiar with these terms:

- **Fractions with unlike denominators** (a.k.a. "unlike fractions") have denominators that are not the same.
- **Fractions with like denominators** (a.k.a "like fractions") have denominators that are the same.

Children in fifth grade understand that unlike denominators/fractions cannot be added or subtracted. Adding thirds and fifths, for example, is like adding apples and oranges….you first have to decide on a common label. If you add 2 apples + 3 oranges, you end up with 5 *fruits*. So to add thirds and fifths, first both fractions must be rewritten with a common denominator.

©2016 Conceptual Learning Associates

Example:

$$\frac{2}{3} + \frac{3}{5} = ?$$

In this example, a common denominator could be any common multiple of 5 and 3. In this case we will use 15. Although 30, 45, 60 and many others are acceptable, the common practice is to use the least (lowest) multiple.

The ideal scenario is for children to be *fluent in the basic multiplication facts*…this makes "thinking" of a common multiple quite easy.

For students who struggle, a common practice is to simply multiply the given denominators and use that product as the common denominator.

Once a common denominator is decided on, children create equivalent fractions. (This builds directly on the work children did in grade 4.)

$$\frac{2}{3} \times \frac{5}{5} = \frac{10}{15} \qquad \frac{3}{5} \times \frac{3}{3} = \frac{9}{15}$$

Now that they have like fractions, they can simply replace the original fractions and then add or subtract.

$$\frac{10}{15} + \frac{9}{15} = \frac{19}{15} \text{ or } 1\frac{4}{15}$$

or

$$\frac{10}{15} - \frac{9}{15} = \frac{1}{15}$$

*Important to note here is that leaving a sum or difference as a fraction greater than 1 (you may remember them as "improper fractions") is acceptable AS LONG AS THE CONTEXT of the question allows for it. For example, we would not say $\frac{5}{2}$ (five halves) gallons of milk…in this case "converting" to the mixed number $2\frac{1}{2}$ gallons is contextually appropriate.

©2016 Conceptual Learning Associates

Example:

$$7\frac{3}{5} - 4\frac{1}{2} = ?$$

$$7\frac{3}{5} = 7\frac{6}{10}$$

$$-4\frac{1}{2} = -4\frac{5}{10}$$

$$3\frac{1}{10}$$

Make equivalent fractions using a common denominator-(see example on previous page). In this example fifths and halves are replaced by tenths. Children then "subtract as usual." Notice that the whole numbers, 7 and 4, remain the same.

©2016 Conceptual Learning Associates

Example:

$$5\frac{1}{8} - 2\frac{3}{4} = \ ?$$

Equivalent fractions found using a common denominator (see example on previous page). In this example children understand they cannot subtract $\frac{6}{8}$ *from* $\frac{1}{8}$. They employ the subtraction strategy of re-grouping (borrowing).

$$5\frac{1}{8} = 5\frac{1}{8}$$
$$-\ 2\frac{3}{4} = 2\frac{6}{8}$$

Children "borrow" one whole from the 5 so it is now 4. The one whole that is borrowed is made into a fraction that equals one (whatever the common denominator is…in this case it is $\frac{8}{8}$) This is then *added* to the fraction that is "already there" (in this case $\frac{1}{8}$). At this point children can easily subtract.

$$4\frac{8}{8}$$

$$5\frac{1}{8} + \frac{8}{8} = \frac{9}{8}$$

$$-\ 2\frac{6}{8}$$

$$2\frac{3}{8}$$

©2016 Conceptual Learning Associates

Example:

Children may be more comfortable adding and subtracting using fractions greater than one instead of mixed numbers.

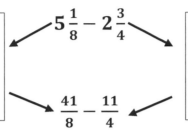

$$5\frac{1}{8} - 2\frac{3}{4}$$

5 wholes broken into eighths (denominator) yields $\frac{40}{8} + \frac{1}{8}$ that is remaining gives $\frac{41}{8}$

2 wholes broken into fourths (denominator) yields $\frac{8}{4} + \frac{3}{4}$ that are remaining gives $\frac{11}{4}$

$$\frac{41}{8} - \frac{11}{4}$$

$$\frac{41}{8} - \frac{22}{8}$$

Find common denominator and "make" equivalent fractions. (In this case one of the existing denominators, 8, becomes the common denominator so only one fraction needs to be replaced.) Children can complete these steps in *ANY* order! They can choose the way that makes the most sense.

$$\frac{41}{8} - \frac{22}{8} = \frac{19}{8} \ or \ 2\frac{3}{8}$$

(How an answer is expressed depends on the context.)

Simply subtract as normal. Addition follows the same thinking!

65

Example:

$$5\frac{1}{8} - 2\frac{3}{4}$$

Children with a greater conceptual understanding may just decide to count on, after equivalent fractions are made, from the lesser number.

A child solving this problem might reason like this, "I can represent $2\frac{3}{4}$ as $2\frac{6}{8}$ because they are equivalent fractions. Then both numbers have the same denominator making it simple to count on and find the difference."

$$2\frac{6}{8} \xrightarrow{\;+\;\frac{2}{8}\;} 3$$

| Add a fraction to the lesser number to make the next whole. |

$$5\frac{1}{8} \xrightarrow{\;-\,3\;} 2\frac{1}{8}$$

| Subtract the whole from the greater number. |

$$\frac{2}{8} + 2\frac{1}{8} = 2\frac{3}{8}$$

| Find the sum of the two numbers and you have your difference. |

©2016 Conceptual Learning Associates

Fraction Addition

and Subtraction Word Problems

Learning standard 5.NF.2 says:

Solve word problems involving addition and subtraction of fractions referring to the same whole, including cases of unlike denominators, e.g., by using visual fraction models or equations to represent the problem. Use benchmark fractions and number sense of fractions to estimate mentally and assess the reasonableness of answers. For example, recognize an incorrect result 2/5 + 1/2 = 3/7, by observing that 3/7 < 1/2

What it means:

To mentally estimate the values of various fractions, fourth graders learned to use the "benchmark fractions" strategy.

- **Benchmark Fractions:** Familiar fractions such as one half, one fourth, three fourths, or 1 whole that children use in order to plot or locate other, less familiar fractions, on a number line. The familiar placement of these fractions makes them act as "landmarks", allowing children to more easily determine where the other fractions should be placed.

Fifth graders use this benchmark fractions strategy when they add and subtract to solve fraction word problems. First they visualize where each fraction in the problem would sit on a number line, in relation to the familiar fractions. After visualizing and reasoning about the value of each fraction, children are able to estimate sums and differences. These estimates help them determine whether or not their answers are reasonable.

When solving word problems involving the addition and subtraction of fractions, fifth graders use all of their understanding fraction addition and subtraction. They may be asked to work with like or unlike denominators, simple fractions or mixed numbers.

©2016 Conceptual Learning Associates

Example:

Jim ate $\frac{3}{6}$ of a dark chocolate bar, and $\frac{3}{4}$ of an equal-size milk chocolate bar. How many bars of chocolate did Jim eat?

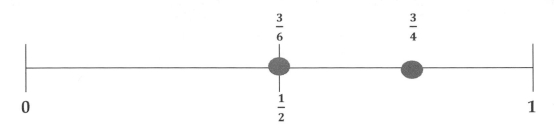

A child solving this problem might reason like this, "I know that $\frac{3}{6}$ is equal to one half, and that $\frac{3}{4}$ is more than a half but less than one whole. When I add them together, I should get a total that is more than one since I'm adding a half and a little more than a half."

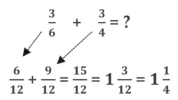

$$\frac{3}{6} + \frac{3}{4} = ?$$

$$\frac{6}{12} + \frac{9}{12} = \frac{15}{12} = 1\frac{3}{12} = 1\frac{1}{4}$$

After adding the fractions he or she might continue to think, "Since $1\frac{1}{4}$ is just a bit more than 1 whole it is a reasonable answer!"

Jim ate $1\frac{1}{4}$ bars of chocolate.

*Note: In the above example the solution of $1\frac{3}{12}$ was simplified to $1\frac{1}{4}$ because it made sense to do so within the context of the problem. (We wouldn't measure the amount of chocolate Jim ate in twelfths.)

©2016 Conceptual Learning Associates

Fractions as Division

Learning standard 5.NF.3 says:

Interpret a fraction as division of the numerator by the denominator (a/b = a ÷ b). Solve word problems involving division of whole numbers leading to answers in the form of fractions or mixed numbers, e.g., by using visual fraction models or equations to represent the problem. For example, interpret 3/4 as the result of dividing 3 by 4, noting that 3/4 multiplied by 4 equals 3, and that when 3 wholes are shared equally among 4 people each person has a share of size 3/4. If 9 people want to share a 50-pound sack of rice equally by weight, how many pounds of rice should each person get? Between what two whole numbers does your answer lie?

What it means:

Children formally worked with division for the first time in grade 4, learning that division creates equal groups, or means "equal sharing" of things. In fifth grade, this idea of equal sharing is the foundation for a deeper understanding of fractions. Fifth graders develop the connection between fractions and division, eventually coming to the understanding that any fraction can be viewed as a division problem, with the numerator being divided by the denominator.

This is a shift from fourth grade thinking, where the numerator and denominators were simply naming "the number of parts we have over the number of parts in the whole". This thinking worked in fourth grade because children only worked with fractional situations where "the whole" was always only 1 item (ONE pizza being split up into equal parts, ONE book being read in equal size chapters, ONE length of ribbon being cut into equal size pieces , etc.) In fifth grade children are exposed to situations where "the whole amount" of something is comprised of more than one whole. For example, 5 friends sharing 3 chocolate bars: In this example the whole amount being divided is comprised of 3 whole chocolate bars. In this case 3 (chocolate bars) is being divided by 5 (friends), which can be expressed as $\frac{3}{5}$.

©2016 Conceptual Learning Associates

<u>This thinking begins with a familiar concept:</u>

A family of 6 equally sharing 1 granola bar.

1 granola bar

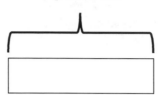

1 granola bar

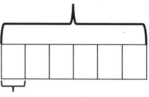

Equally divided into 6 pieces (each piece represents 1 family member's share)

Each piece has a value of $\frac{1}{6}$

Each family member will have $\frac{1}{6}$ of the granola bar.

©2016 Conceptual Learning Associates

The shift in the fifth grade is the "sharing" (division) of *more than 1 whole* with any number.

....So the thinking then shifts to:

Six people sharing three granola bars.

3 granola bars

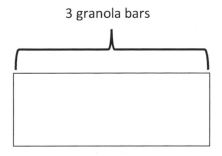

3 granola bars

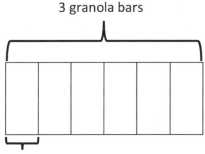

Equally divided into 6 pieces (each piece represents 1 family member's share)

Each piece has a value of $\frac{3}{6}$
which is the same as 3 ÷ 6

We are simply dividing 3 into six equal groups; 3 ÷ 6 (an expression), children learn that a fraction bar *means* division. So 3 ÷ 6 can simply be written as $\frac{3}{6}$.

In this example each piece has a value of $\frac{3}{6}$.

There are 6 pieces so $\frac{3}{6}$ x 6 = $\frac{18}{6}$ which is equivalent to 3.

This thinking applies to ANY division example, $15 \div 5 = \frac{15}{5} = 3$.

©2016 Conceptual Learning Associates

Example:

Six friends go hiking. They evenly split 9 granola bars. How many granola bars does each person get?

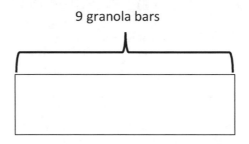

9 granola bars

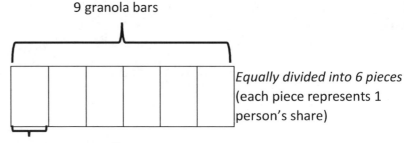

9 granola bars

Equally divided into 6 pieces (each piece represents 1 person's share)

Each piece has a value of $\frac{9}{6}$

which is the same as; 9 ÷ 6

Each person will get $\frac{9}{6}$ = $1\frac{3}{6}$ or $1\frac{1}{2}$ granola bars.

This is an example of employing "reducing" or "simplifying" within a context. We would rarely, if ever, work with $\frac{9}{6}$, or $1\frac{3}{6}$ granola bars.

Within the context of the question $1\frac{1}{2}$ makes the most sense.

©2016 Conceptual Learning Associates

Fraction Multiplication

Learning standard 5.NF.4 says:

Apply and extend previous understandings of multiplication to multiply a fraction or whole number by a fraction. Interpret the product (a/b) × q as a parts of a partition of q into b equal parts; equivalently, as the result of a sequence of operations a × q ÷ b. For example, use a visual fraction model to show (2/3) × 4 = 8/3, and create a story context for this equation. Do the same with (2/3) × (4/5) = 8/15. (In general, (a/b) × (c/d) = ac/bd.)

Find the area of a rectangle with fractional side lengths by tiling it with unit squares of the appropriate unit fraction side lengths, and show that the area is the same as would be found by multiplying the side lengths. Multiply fractional side lengths to find areas of rectangles, and represent fraction products as rectangular areas.

What it means:

Fourth graders initially learned the concept of multiplication as "repeated addition". For example "5 x 2" is the same as "5 groups of 2", which is also the same as "2 + 2 + 2 + 2 + 2". Children then used this concept, along with their understanding of fraction addition, as a foundation for multiplying a whole number times a fraction. They came to understand that when they are multiplying a whole number by a fraction, the whole number actually tells how many times the fraction is being added to itself. This means that "5 x $\frac{1}{2}$" is the same as "5 groups of $\frac{1}{2}$", which is also the same as "$\frac{1}{2} + \frac{1}{2} + \frac{1}{2} + \frac{1}{2} + \frac{1}{2}$" or $\frac{5}{2}$. (Children know from their work with fraction addition that since the denominator names the size of the unit, it doesn't change.)

In fifth grade, children build on this foundational work to gain a more broad understanding of fraction multiplication. They use reasoning and modeling in order multiply fractions by both whole numbers and other fractions.

All of the work fifth graders do with multiplication is done based on understanding and modeling. In this way, they are able to understand how fraction multiplication works without needing to memorize "fraction multiplication steps". The big idea here is for children to "discover" that when they multiply a fraction by a whole number, they can simply multiply the numerator of the fraction by the whole number, and keep the denominator the same. Similarly, they "discover" that to multiply a fraction by another fraction they simply need to multiply the numerators and then multiply the

©2016 Conceptual Learning Associates

denominators. By discovering this "shortcut" on their own, AFTER they understand the reasoning, and because they have not memorized "steps" which are easily forgotten, children are much more likely to remember this concept.

When children first multiplied fractions, they learned that the multiplication symbol stood for the words "groups of". Some children might learn this same concept using the words "copies of". In this way, $5 \times \frac{1}{2}$ was also read as *"5 copies of $\frac{1}{2}$"*. Later this was shortened to simply *"of"*. Since fifth graders understand this concept, we use it to begin the topic of fraction multiplication.

©2016 Conceptual Learning Associates

Example:

$$\frac{3}{4} \, of \, 8$$

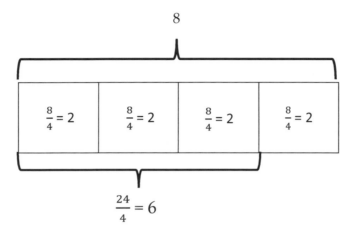

In this model, "three fourths of eight" is interpreted as *eight being broken into four parts and we're working with three of the four*. If eight is broken into four equal parts, there will be two in each part. Taking three of the parts means 2 x 3 or 6.

$$\frac{3}{4} \, of \, 8 \, is \, 6$$

©2016 Conceptual Learning Associates

Example:

$$\frac{4}{5} \; of \; 20$$

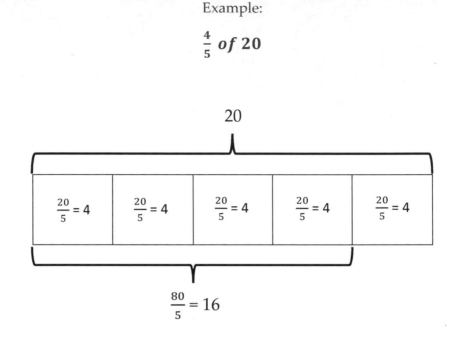

A child solving this problem might think, "Four fifths of 20 means that 20 is being broken into fifths, and we are taking 4 of the fifths. If twenty is broken into 5 equal parts (fifths), there are 4 in each part. Taking 4 of the parts means 4 x 4 or 16.

$$\frac{4}{5} \; of \; 20 \; is \; 16$$

©2016 Conceptual Learning Associates

Example:

A different question entirely!

$\frac{3}{5}$ of a number is 30. What is the number?

Fifth graders are able to use their understanding of parts and wholes to answer similar questions! In this case, we know the number of parts, as well as the amount in each part.

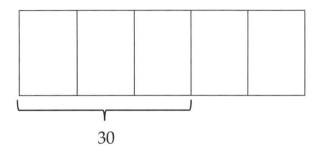

30

A child solving this problem might reason like this, "Since I don't know the total but I do know that three equal parts total 30, I can divide to find the amount in just one part."

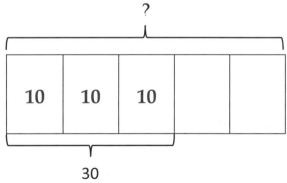

30

Once I know that each part is 10, I just have to multiply it by the total number of parts in the figure...in this case 5. 10 x 5 = 50

3 (out of the 5) equal 30

So each (fifth) must equal 10...making the total 50.

©2016 Conceptual Learning Associates

$$\frac{3}{4} \times 4$$

(now "of" is simply "replaced by a multiplication sign)

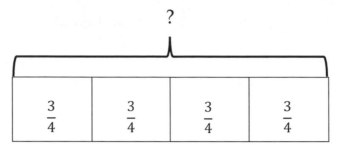

$$\frac{3}{4} + \frac{3}{4} + \frac{3}{4} + \frac{3}{4} = \frac{12}{4} = 3$$

Children are familiar with the concept of multiplication being presented as a "number of groups".

$\frac{3}{4} \times 4 = \frac{3}{4}$ of 4 **or** 4 groups of $\frac{3}{4}$

A child solving this problem might decide to use what they know about the Commutative property. Children understand that when they add or multiply the order of the items being added or multiplied may be changed without changing the total. In this case, the child has chosen to interpret the problem to read "4 groups of $\frac{3}{4}$. Once this decision was made, the child had the choice to multiply $4 \times \frac{3}{4}$ or add $\frac{3}{4}$ four times. Either way is perfectly correct…children should do whichever is more comfortable and efficient.

$$\frac{3}{4} \times 4 = \frac{12}{4} = 3$$

©2016 Conceptual Learning Associates

Example:

$$\frac{3}{4} \text{x } 8$$

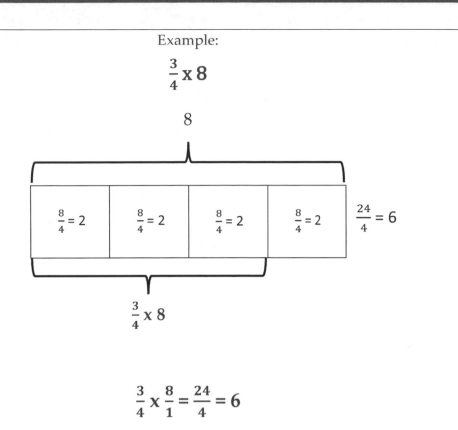

$$\frac{3}{4} \text{x } \frac{8}{1} = \frac{24}{4} = 6$$

*This problem follows the same procedure as the one found on page 75. The difference here is that a multiplication sign has replaced the word "of" in the problem.

79

©2016 Conceptual Learning Associates

When children first learned to multiply they used an *area model*. (See Grade 4 multiplication models.) The area model is based on what children know about the area formula: That the area of a rectangle is found by multiplying its length and width. This same model is used in fifth grade to model fraction multiplication.

Important to note: A square is used here to model fraction multiplication. This is done because both fractions should be representing the same 1 whole. Using a square allows us to represent an area of "1". Children may or may not draw squares when they work with this model…their models may look more rectangular. While not "mathematically perfect", these rectangles will work just fine.

Example:

$$\frac{1}{2} \times \frac{3}{4}$$

Begin by dividing the model in half, and shade one part to represent a side length of $\frac{1}{2}$.

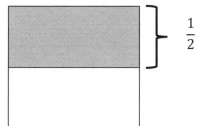

©2016 Conceptual Learning Associates

Then divide the model in fourths, in the opposite direction, and shade three parts to represent a side length of $\frac{3}{4}$.

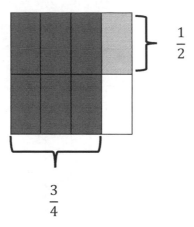

$$\frac{3}{4}$$

The area where the shaded regions overlap represents the product of the two fractions. In this case, we can look at the overlapping region as either "one half of three fourths" or "three fourths of one half". Either way, children can SEE that the product is $\frac{3}{8}$ of the whole.

The product is where both shaded parts overlap... in this case 3 out of the 8 pieces overlap; so

$$\frac{1}{2} \times \frac{3}{4} = \frac{3}{8}$$

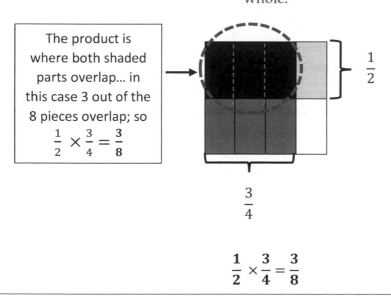

$$\frac{1}{2} \times \frac{3}{4} = \frac{3}{8}$$

81

©2016 Conceptual Learning Associates

$$1\frac{3}{4} \times \frac{2}{3} =$$

We start with two squares here because each one represents 1 whole, and the first term being multiplied, $1\frac{3}{4}$, is greater than one.

Each whole broken into fourths. Seven parts are shaded to represent one whole (4 parts) and three fourths of another whole (3 parts) for a total length of $1\frac{3}{4}$.

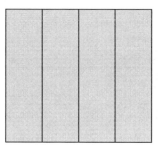
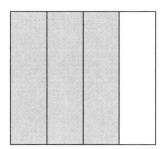

©2016 Conceptual Learning Associates

$$1\frac{3}{4} \text{ x } \frac{2}{3}$$

Next, each whole is broken into thirds, and 2 parts of each are shaded to represent a length of $\frac{2}{3}$.

 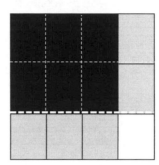

The "double shaded" (black) part, where the shading overlaps, is the product. In this model, children are able to SEE that the product is 14 double-shaded parts when each whole is divided into 12, or $\frac{14}{12}$.

$$1\frac{3}{4} \text{ x } \frac{2}{3} = \frac{14}{12} = 1\frac{2}{12}$$

©2016 Conceptual Learning Associates

Over time, children "discover" that the area model is representing the same thing they get when they simply multiply the numerators and then multiply the denominators. For this to work, children have two choices: either they first represent mixed numbers as fractions greater than one and multiply, or they break the mixed numbers apart and multiply separately before adding the separate products.

In this case $1\frac{3}{4}$ *was rewritten as* $\frac{7}{4}$ before multiplying.

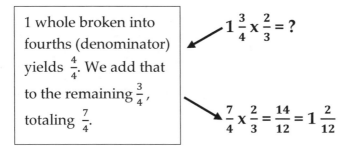

1 whole broken into fourths (denominator) yields $\frac{4}{4}$. We add that to the remaining $\frac{3}{4}$, totaling $\frac{7}{4}$.

$$1\frac{3}{4} \times \frac{2}{3} = ?$$

$$\frac{7}{4} \times \frac{2}{3} = \frac{14}{12} = 1\frac{2}{12}$$

In this case $1\frac{3}{4}$ was broken apart and the parts multiplied separately.

$$1\frac{3}{4} \times \frac{2}{3} =$$

$$(1 \times \frac{2}{3}) + (\frac{3}{4} \times \frac{2}{3}) =$$

$$\frac{2}{3} + \frac{6}{12} =$$

$$\frac{8}{12} + \frac{6}{12} = \frac{14}{12} = 1\frac{2}{12}$$

©2016 Conceptual Learning Associates

Multiplication as Scaling

Learning standard 5.NF.5 says:

Interpret multiplication as scaling (resizing), by:
Comparing the size of a product to the size of one factor on the basis of the size of the other factor, without performing the indicated multiplication.
Explaining why multiplying a given number by a fraction greater than 1 results in a product greater than the given number (recognizing multiplication by whole numbers greater than 1 as a familiar case); explaining why multiplying a given number by a fraction less than 1 results in a product smaller than the given number; and relating the principle of fraction equivalence a/b = (n × a)/(n × b) to the effect of multiplying a/b by 1.

What it means:

The first meaning of multiplication children were exposed to, in grade 3, was the repeated addition of equal groups. For example, 3 x 4 meant "three groups of 4" or 4 + 4 + 4. In fourth grade children learned the meaning of multiplication comparison. For example, 3 x 4 meant "three times as many as 4". In both cases, children were working with whole numbers, which always resulted in a product that was greater than either of the two numbers being multiplied.

Fifth graders combine and build on both of these meanings as they work with multiplication as *scaling*. Because they are now multiplying whole numbers by fractions as well as other whole numbers, they learn that the product might be greater OR LESS than the numbers being multiplied. The big idea is for fifth graders to determine, WITHOUT ACUTALLY MULTIPLYING, whether the product would be greater or less than the numbers in the problem IF they were to multiply. To do this, children see the second number in the problem, the 4 in our example of 3 x 4, as the *quantity* being worked with. They see the first number in the problem, the 3, as the *scaling factor*. If the scaling factor (first number) is greater than 1, then the product will be greater than the quantity (second number). If the scaling factor is a fraction less than 1, then the product will be less than the quantity.

For example, 3 x 4 would yield a product greater than 4 because the scaling factor (3) is greater than 1. The resulting product would be 3 times as much as 4. Multiplying $\frac{1}{3}$ x 4,

85

©2016 Conceptual Learning Associates

however, would yield a product less than 4 because the scaling factor is a fraction less than 1. The resulting product would be one third of 4.

Over time, and with practice, fifth grade children "see" that whenever they multiply any quantity by a number less than one they produce a smaller quantity. Conversely, when they multiply any quantity by a number greater than 1 they produce a larger quantity. Children in fifth grade go on to apply this thinking to problem solving situations.

This fifth grade shift to seeing multiplication as scaling is a foundation skill for the work children will do in grade 6 with ratios and proportional reasoning.

©2016 Conceptual Learning Associates

Example:

The drawing below shows the length and width measurements of a rectangle.

1 unit

*Image not drawn to scale.

1 unit

THINK: *Is the area of this rectangle greater than, less than, or equal to 1?*

(It's equal to 1 because 1 x 1 is 1 square unit.)

1. Is the area of the rectangle below greater or less than the one at the top of the page? Use numbers, pictures or words to explain your thinking.

1 unit

*Image not drawn to scale.

a fraction greater than 1

It must be greater because a fraction greater than 1 x 1 has to be more than 1 square unit. (The scaling factor has increased.)

2. Is the area of the rectangle below greater or less than the one at the top of the page? Use numbers, pictures or words to explain your thinking.

1 unit

*Image not drawn to scale.

a fraction less than 1

It is less than because a fraction less than 1 x 1 has to be less than 1 square unit. (The scaling factor has decreased.)

87

©2016 Conceptual Learning Associates

Problem Solving with Fraction Multiplication

Learning standard 5.NF.6 says:

Solve real world problems involving multiplication of fractions and mixed numbers, e.g., by using visual fraction models or equations to represent the problem.

What it means:

To solve word problems involving fraction multiplication, fifth graders use everything they understand about multiplying fractions. Children may use models and/or numbers & equations to solve these problems. The big idea is that children in fifth grade are able to solve the problems and then use reasoning to determine whether or not their answers make sense.

Example:

A chocolate cookie recipe will make 36 cookies. This recipe needs $4\frac{1}{2}$ cups of flour. Olivia wants to make 18 cookies. How many cups of flour will she need?

$4\frac{1}{2}$ cups of flour = 36 cookies

? cups of flour = 18 cookies

$$4\frac{1}{2} \times \frac{1}{2} = ? \text{ OR } \frac{1}{2} \text{ of } 4\frac{1}{2} = ?$$

$$\frac{9}{2} \times \frac{1}{2} = \frac{9}{4} = 2\frac{1}{4}$$

Or

$$(4 \times \frac{1}{2}) + (\frac{1}{2} \times \frac{1}{2})$$

$$2 + \frac{1}{4} = 2\frac{1}{4}$$

Olivia will need $2\frac{1}{4}$ cups of flour.

©2016 Conceptual Learning Associates

Dividing Fractions by Whole Numbers

Learning standard 5.NF.7 says:

Apply and extend previous understandings of division to divide unit fractions by whole numbers and whole numbers by unit fractions.

Interpret division of a unit fraction by a non-zero whole number, and compute such quotients. For example, create a story context for (1/3) ÷ 4, and use a visual fraction model to show the quotient. Use the relationship between multiplication and division to explain that (1/3) ÷ 4 = 1/12 because (1/12) × 4 = 1/3.

Interpret division of a whole number by a unit fraction, and compute such quotients. For example, create a story context for 4 ÷ (1/5), and use a visual fraction model to show the quotient. Use the relationship between multiplication and division to explain that 4 ÷ (1/5) = 20 because 20 × (1/5) = 4.

Solve real world problems involving division of unit fractions by non-zero whole numbers and division of whole numbers by unit fractions, e.g., by using visual fraction models and equations to represent the problem. For example, how much chocolate will each person get if 3 people share 1/2 lb. of chocolate equally? How many 1/3-cup servings are in 2 cups of raisins?

What it means:

Fifth graders are introduced to fraction division for the first time. They divide fractions by whole numbers, as well as whole numbers by fractions. To do this, children rely on their understanding of the relationship between multiplication and division. They understand, for example, that $6 ÷ 3 = 2$ and that the related multiplication fact is the inverse of this statement, or $6 = 3 \times 2$ or $2 \times 3 = 6$.

In a very similar fashion, fifth graders are able to reason that $\frac{1}{4} ÷ 6 = \frac{1}{24}$ because when they work in reverse, $\frac{1}{24} \times 6 = \frac{6}{24} or \frac{1}{4}$. The important thing here is that the work fifth graders do with division of fractions *MUST be built on their understanding of how division works and what makes sense. They MUST conceptually understand the thinking behind fraction division.* Teachers and parents are usually familiar with the "keep' change, switch" strategy that many of us learned as students. Unfortunately, we never learned how or why this strategy worked. If you are scratching your head trying to remember either A) how to divide fractions, or B) what "keep, change, switch" means, then you probably learned fraction division this way…and worse, you probably don't remember it!! This is exactly what we want to avoid. Simply teaching children to

©2016 Conceptual Learning Associates

"change" a division sentence to a multiplication sentence as long as they "flip" one of the fractions will NOT HELP children understand and identify when to divide.

Children in fifth grade often struggle with differentiating between multiplication and division when working with fractions. The underlying MEANING of each problem, and truly understanding how each operation affects the numbers in the problem, is what will help children solve these word problems correctly.

©2016 Conceptual Learning Associates

Example:

$$5 \div \frac{1}{6} = ?$$

The goal is for children to understand that $5 \div \frac{1}{6} = 30$ because $30 \times \frac{1}{6} = 5$.

It is helpful if children create a situation for each equation, based on the operation:

For example:

This *division* equation is asking if we have 5 wholes and were to divide each of them into sixths, *how many sixths would we have*?

We would have 30 sixths.

The inverse *multiplication* equation is asking what 30 times one sixth is equal (or equivalent) to?

30 sixths ($\frac{30}{6}$) equals 5 wholes.

©2016 Conceptual Learning Associates

Example:

$$\frac{1}{6} \div 5 = ?$$

The goal is for children to understand that when a fraction (less than one) is divided, it must be viewed in reference to 1 whole. The easiest way to do this is to begin with a fraction bar, broken into the appropriate fractional parts, in this case, sixths.

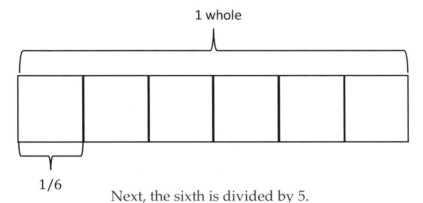

Next, the sixth is divided by 5.

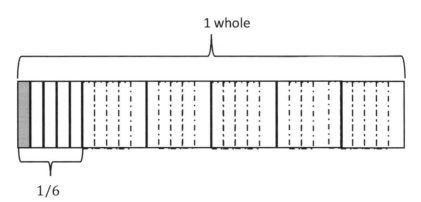

Since this problem is solved in reference to 1 whole, we next imagine that each of the sixths gets divided into fifths, making a total of 30 equal sections. When $\frac{1}{6}$ is divided by 5, each one of the sections is equal to $\frac{1}{30}$ of the whole.

$$\frac{1}{6} \div 5 = \frac{1}{30}$$

©2016 Conceptual Learning Associates

The inverse *multiplication* equation is asking what $\frac{1}{30}$ times five is equal to.

$$\frac{1}{30} \ x \ 5 = 5 \ x \frac{1}{30} = \frac{5}{30} \ or \frac{1}{6}.$$

The relationship between division and multiplication **is crucial** to children's understanding of these concepts.

The foundation for this thinking has been cemented in all of the fraction work that children have done up to this point.

Examples:

$$1 \div \frac{1}{7} = ?$$

A child solving this problem should reason, "How many sevenths (denominator) is one whole divided into?"

7 equal pieces (denominator) make 1 whole.

$$\text{So } 1 \div \frac{1}{7} = 7$$

$$3 \div \frac{1}{7} = ?$$

How many sevenths are in 3 wholes?

3 wholes are **each** divided into seven pieces (sevenths).

$$\text{So } 3 \div \frac{1}{7} = 21$$

93

©2016 Conceptual Learning Associates

Example:

15 people are attending a party. For dessert the baker is making chocolate chip cupcakes. She has 6 cups of chocolate chips. Each cupcake requires $\frac{1}{3}$ of a cup of chocolate chips. If each person receives one cupcake, does the baker have enough chocolate chips?

$$6 \div \frac{1}{3} = ?$$

Think: *How many thirds are in 6?*

A child solving this problem might think," I know that there are 3 thirds in one whole, so there are 6 thirds in two wholes, and 18 thirds in 6 wholes. So 6 cups of chocolate chips divided by one third equals 18 thirds."

$$6 \div \frac{1}{3} = 18$$

He or she might go on to think, "If each person gets a cupcake and there are 15 people, they need 15 cupcakes. The baker has enough chips to make 18 cupcakes. So, yes, the baker has enough chips."

Yes, the baker has enough chips to make at least 15 cupcakes.

©2016 Conceptual Learning Associates

GRADE 5- EXPRESSIONS AND EQUATIONS

By meeting the learning standards in this section, fifth grade children will show that they:

Understand how parentheses, brackets and braces are used in mathematical expressions.

Are able to evaluate expressions that contain parentheses, brackets and braces.

Writing and Interpreting Expressions

Learning standard 5.OA.1 says:

Use parentheses, brackets, or braces in numerical expressions, and evaluate expressions with these symbols.

Learning standard 5.OA.2 says:

Write simple expressions that record calculations with numbers, and interpret numerical expressions without evaluating them. For example, express the calculation "add 8 and 7, then multiply by 2" as $2 \times (8 + 7)$. Recognize that $3 \times (18932 + 921)$ is three times as large as $18932 + 921$, without having to calculate the indicated sum or product.

What they mean:

In fifth grade children begin more formal work with expressions. They use symbols, such as parentheses, to write expressions that represent a "plan for calculations" or "calculation agenda". Children in fifth grade build on work they've done in earlier grades, writing number sentences (expressions) to represent word problem situations. Fifth graders understand that the expressions they write represent *a plan* for doing calculations.

In order to successfully write expressions containing more than one calculation, children in fifth grade understand and use the Order of Operations. They use parentheses, brackets or braces in order to show the order in which the operations in the equations should be performed. To represent the calculation "subtract 2 from 9, then multiply by 6", for example, a fifth grader would write "6 x (9 – 2)"….understanding that using the parentheses in this manner means that 2 is subtracted from 9 before anything is multiplied by 6.

In addition to writing expressions, children in fifth grade also understand how to interpret them. They know that the same order of operations they use when writing expressions also applies when determining the meaning of an expression. For example, given the expression "4 x (65,723 – 457)" a fifth grader interprets it as "four times as much as 65,723 – 457" (again the work in parentheses is performed first). They are able to make this interpretation before or even without doing the actual calculations. The focus here is on the understanding of what the expression represents.

©2016 Conceptual Learning Associates

The work that fifth grade children do with expressions lays an important foundation. Developing these understandings now prepares children for all of the Expressions and Equations work they will do in grades 6, 7 and 8.

Example:

Write the numerical expression for the following. Then solve.

3 times the difference between 347.9 and 79.3

A child solving this equation might think, "I have to multiply the difference between the two decimal numbers by 3. That means I need to find the difference first, and then do the multiplication."

"When I write the expression I should put 347.9 – 79.3 in parentheses. The operation placed inside the parentheses is done first."

3 x (347.9 – 79.3)

"To solve this problem I have to subtract first, because the subtraction is inside of the parentheses. Then I can multiply the difference by 3."

347.9 – 79.3 = 268.6

268.6 x 3 = 805.8

3 times the difference between 347.9 and 79.3 is 805.8

97

Example:

Write the following numerical expression in words. Then solve.

(23.5 + 13.6) x 11

One child solving this problem might think, "This expression is representing 11 times what is in the parentheses. Inside the parentheses two numbers are being added together. So the sum of the numbers is being multiplied by 11"

11 times as many as the sum of 23.5 and 13.6

A second child might reason slightly differently like this, "The sum of the number in the parentheses is being multiplied by 11.

The sum of 23.5 and 13.6 times 11

Either of these is correct.

To solve, it is important that the work inside the parentheses is completed first.

23.5 + 13.6 = 37.1

Then the sum is multiplied by 11

37.1 x 11 = 408.1

(23.5 + 13.6) x 11 = 408.1

©2016 Conceptual Learning Associates

Example:

Write an expression to represent the following problem. Then solve.

A candy factory makes 935 chocolate bars each hour. They make 625 more lollipops each hour than they make chocolate bars. How many lollipops do they make in 8 hours?

To solve this problem a child thinks, "Before I figure out how many lollipops the factory makes in 8 hours, I need to know how many it makes in 1 hour. Every hour the factory makes "625 more than 935" lollipops. That means I need to combine 625 and 935."

(625 + 935)

"Since the sum of 625 and 935 tells how many lollipops are made in 1 hour, that sum must be multiplied by 8 to find out how many are made in 8 hours."

(625 + 935) × 8

Or

8 × (625 + 935)

To solve, the operation in the parentheses is performed first.

625 + 935 = 1560

Then the sum is multiplied by 8.

1560 × 8 = 12,480

(625 + 935) × 8 = 12,480

The candy factory makes 12,480 lollipops in 8 hours.

©2016 Conceptual Learning Associates

GRADE 5-GEOMETRIC MEASUREMENT

By meeting the learning standards in this section, fifth grade children will show that they:

Understand the concept of volume and how it is measured.

Know how to find the volume of a right rectangular prism by packing it with cubes.

Recognize how addition and multiplication can be used to determine volume.

Create and use formulas to find volume.

Exploring Volume

Learning standard 5.MD.3 says:

Recognize volume as an attribute of solid figures and understand concepts of volume measurement.
A cube with side length 1 unit, called a "unit cube," is said to have "one cubic unit" of volume, and can be used to measure volume.
A solid figure which can be packed without gaps or overlaps using n unit cubes is said to have a volume of n cubic units.

What it means:

Fifth grade children explore volume measurement for the first time. They work with three-dimensional figures and recognize that the space inside these shapes can be measured in units called cubes. Each unit cube is 1 unit long, 1 unit wide and 1 unit deep. (The "unit" can be any measurement unit. Children may, for example, measure volume with 1-inch cubes, 1-cenitmeter cubes, 1-foot cubes, etc.)

When finding volume, children understand that volume measurements are expressed in cubic units (or units cubed). This makes sense since volume is a measure of how many unit cubes completely fill the inside of a three-dimensional shape. An important connection for children who may be struggling with this idea is area measurement. Children will remember from third and fourth grade work that area measurements are expressed in square units. This is because the area of a two-dimensional figure is the number of unit squares that completely fills the inside of the shape. Fifth graders are able to reason that when a measurement is made with unit squares, it is expressed in "square units". Likewise, when a measurement is made with unit cubes, it is expressed in "cubic units".

Example:

 = 1 *unit cube* (can be any unit – cm, m, inch, foot, etc.)

This cube measures 1 unit x (by) 1 unit x (by) 1 unit

(1 unit in length, 1 unit in width, and 1 unit in depth)

 - This unit cube has a *volume* (capacity) of *one cubic unit*.

 The volume of this figure is 4 cubic units.

©2016 Conceptual Learning Associates

Measuring Volume

Learning standard 5.MD.4 says:

Measure volumes by counting unit cubes, using cubic cm, cubic in, cubic ft, and improvised units.

What it means:

When fifth graders begin measuring the volume of three-dimensional figures, they start by packing (filling) shapes with unit cubes. Children know that they can simply count the number of cubes inside to find the figure's volume.

Example:

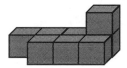 The volume of this figure is 8 cubic units.

Children understand that when they are packing shapes to determine volume, it is important that there be no gaps or overlapping. In order to find an accurate measure of volume, all of the space inside of the shape must be filled with cubes. The most efficient way for children to account for all of the space is to stack the cubes in even layers.

Some children may "see" the layers as equal rows, stacked horizontally. Others may "see" the layers as equal columns, stacked vertically. Either way is correct, as either one will lead children to the correct volume.

Example:

Children measure volume by "stacking" cubes vertically and horizontally without any gaps or overlapping

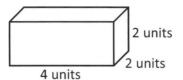
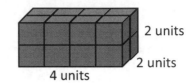

Volume (*v*) = 16 cubic units

Stack 2 rows of 8 units or 2 columns of 8 units.

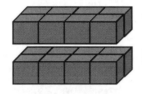

Top (1 row of 8 units)

Bottom (1 row of 8 units)

or

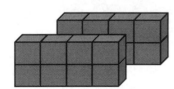

Back (1 column of 8 units)

Front (1 column of 8 units)

or

Four identical 4-unit stacks from left to right

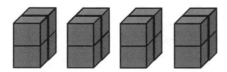

©2016 Conceptual Learning Associates

Example:

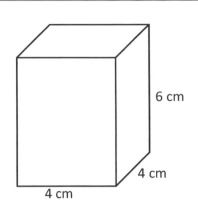 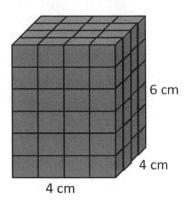

6 cm

4 cm

4 cm

6 cm

4 cm

4 cm

Volume = 96 cubic cm

Stack 6 rows of 16 units **or** 4 columns of 24 units

6 rows of 16 units = 96 cubic units

or

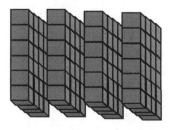

4 columns of 24 units = 96 cubic units

Relating Volume to Multiplication

Learning standard 5.MD.5 says:

Relate volume to the operations of multiplication and addition and solve real world and mathematical problems involving volume.

Find the volume of a right rectangular prism with whole-number side lengths by packing it with unit cubes, and show that the volume is the same as would be found by multiplying the edge lengths, equivalently by multiplying the height by the area of the base. Represent threefold whole-number products as volumes, e.g., to represent the associative property of multiplication

What it means:

Once they are familiar with the concept of packing to find volume, children in fifth grade explore more efficient ways to determine volume. After packing only the bottom layer, children see that they can multiply the length and width to determine the area of the bottom. Once they know that area, they simply have to multiply it by the number of times additional identical layers would be stacked to fill the shape.

When writing the equations they used to find the volume, children see that there are two different ways this can be done:

- One way is to write two equations: one multiplying the length and width, and the second multiplying the result by the number of layers in the height of the shape.

- Another way to mathematically represent finding the volume of the shape is to write one equation multiplying the three numbers in the length, width and height.

This concept develops out of an understanding of how numbers work. Since the earliest grades, children have been recognizing and working with patterns in the way numbers behave. Some children, however, may still have some trouble "seeing" that both of the strategies described here can work. It will help if they solve volume problems using both ways. With enough practice children will see the relationship between the two, and be able to use either one.

©2016 Conceptual Learning Associates

Example:

An order of knee pads is being sent to a sporting goods store in Stony Brook, New York. The knee pads are packaged in 1 foot x 1 foot x 1 foot cubes. The boxes used for shipping are each 4 feet (long) x 4 feet (wide/deep) x 6 feet (tall). How many packages of kneepads will they be able to ship in each box?

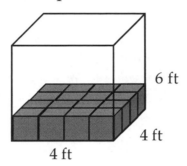

6 ft

4 ft

4 ft

A child solving this problem might think, "Rather than fill the entire prism with cubes I can find the area of the base using cubes and multiply it by the height"

"One way to represent the volume is to first find the area of the bottom layer. Then multiply the area by the height of the shape."

4 ft. x 4 ft. = 16 square ft.

Area of the base is 16 square ft. and there are 6 of these "layers" (height)

16 square ft. x 6 ft. = 96 cubic feet

They will be able to ship 96 packages in each box.

Another child might think, "I multiply the length and width to find the area of the base, and then multiply that by the height, that's the same as multiplying all three numbers. I can write:

4 ft. x 4 ft. x 6 ft. = 96 cubic feet

They will be able to ship 96 packages in each box.

Relating Volume to Multiplication

Learning standard 5.MD.5.B says:

Apply the formulas V = l × w × h and V = b × h for rectangular prisms to find volumes of right rectangular prisms with whole-number edge lengths in the context of solving real world and mathematical problems.

What it means:

Based on the understanding of volume that they've developed, and the strategies they've used to determine the volume of three-dimensional shapes, fifth grade children develop and use two different formulas for finding volume. Formulas are not new to fifth grade children. They first developed formulas for determining area and perimeter in third grade. In fourth grade children used the area formula along with an area model to help them understand multi-digit multiplication.

- *V = b x h (Volume = base x height)*
  *In this case, *b* stands for the *area of the base.*
  Because children understand the idea of stacking identical layers of cubes to find volume, they also know that if they know the area of the base layer they can simply multiply it by the number of layers to find the total volume.

- *V = l x w x h (Volume = length x width x height)*
  Children learn that whenever they know the length, width and height of a figure, they can multiply them in order to determine the volume. They also know that they can multiply them in any order. (This is known as applying the Associative Property of multiplication. Children may or may not know the name of this property, but they do know that changing the order of the factors will not change the product.)

©2016 Conceptual Learning Associates

Example:

An order of knee pads is being sent to a sporting goods store in Stony Brook, New York. The knee pads are packaged in 1 foot x 1 foot x 1 foot cubes. The boxes used for shipping are each 4 feet (long) x 4 feet (wide/deep) x 6 feet (tall). How many packages of kneepads will they be able to ship in each box?

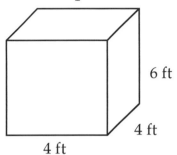

6 ft

4 ft

4 ft

A child finding the volume of this prism might think, "Instead of filling this shape with cubes, I can find the area of the base and multiply it by the height."

$$V = b \times h$$

$$V = 16ft \times 6ft$$

V = 96 cubic feet (feet cubed)

Another child solving this problem might think, "I don't need to fill this figure with cubes, I can simply multiply the length, width and height. The order I multiply them in doesn't matter."

$$V = l \times w \times h$$

$$V = 4ft \times 4ft \times 6ft$$

V = 96 cubic feet (feet cubed)

They can ship 96 packages of kneepads in each box.

Adding Volumes

Learning standard 5.MD.5.C says:

Recognize volume as additive. Find volumes of solid figures composed of two non-overlapping right rectangular prisms by adding the volumes of the non-overlapping parts, applying this technique to solve real world problems.

What it means:

Fifth graders recognize that when a solid figure is made up of two or more figures that do not overlap or have gaps between them, they can find the volume of the entire shape by first finding the volumes of the smaller shapes and then adding them together. This is what we mean when we say that volume is "additive". Children have worked with this principle before. In fourth grade, they learned that angle measure is also additive. When two angles share a side, meaning that they don't overlap or have space between them, the measures of the two smaller angles can be added together to find the total measure of the larger angle.

©2016 Conceptual Learning Associates

Example:

A hobby store needs to display 60 items in this case. Twenty-six of the items are in 2ft by 2ft by 1ft boxes. The remaining 34 items are all packaged in 1 foot cubes. Can this display case hold all of the products?

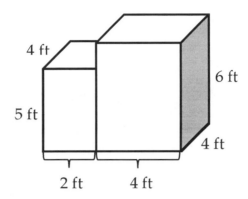

When solving this problem a child might reason like this, "First I need to find the volume of the entire display case so I know how much room there is. Since it's made up of two different size shapes I can find the volume of each one separately and then add them together."

Smaller Figure

$V = l \times w \times h$

$V = 2 \times 4 \times 5$

$V = (2 \times 5) \times 4$

("I know I can change the order of the numbers without changing the total!")

$V = 10 \times 4$

V = 40 cubic feet

Larger Figure

$$V = l \text{ x } w \text{ x } h$$

$$V = 4 \text{ x } (4 \text{ x } 6)$$

("I know it won't change the total if I multiply the last two numbers first!")

$$V = 4 \text{ x } 24$$

$$V = 96 \text{ cubic feet}$$

"Now I need to add them together."

$$96 + 40 = 136$$

The total volume of the display case is 136 cubic feet.

Next the child's reasoning might continue like this, "Now I need to figure out how much space is needed for all of the items. I can do that by adding up the volume needed for each of the two different size boxes."

$$V = l \text{ x } w \text{ x } h$$

$$V = 2 \text{ x } 2 \text{ x } 1$$

$$V = 4 \text{ x } 1$$

$$V = 4 \text{ cubic feet for 1 item}$$

$$26 \text{ x } 4 = 104$$

Twenty-six 2 x 2 x 1 items need 104 cubic feet of space.

©2016 Conceptual Learning Associates

$$V = l \text{ x } w \text{ x } h$$

$$V = 1 \text{ x } 1 \text{ x } 1$$

$$V = 1$$

V = 1 cubic foot for 1 item

34 x 1 = 34

Thirty-four 1 x 1 x 1 items need 34 cubic feet of space.

"Now I need to add them together."

104 + 34 = 138

The total amount of display space needed in 138 cubic feet.

"Finally, I need to compare the amount of space there is with the amount of space needed. The case has 136 cubic feet of space. The items require 138 cubic feet of space."

There is not enough room in the display case for all 60 items.

GRADE 5- GEOMETRY

By meeting the learning standards in this section, fifth grade children will show that they:

Understand that the characteristics pertaining to a group of two-dimensional figures also pertain to all of the sub-groups of that category.

(For example: Squares are a subgroup of rectangles so a square must have all of the characteristics of a rectangle.)

Recognize that quadrilaterals can be arranged in a hierarchy based on their characteristics.

Identifying Figures

Learning standard 5.G.3 says:

Understand that attributes belonging to a category of two-dimensional figures also belong to all subcategories of that category. For example, all rectangles have four right angles and squares are rectangles, so all squares have four right angles.

What it means:

In third grade children were introduced to the idea that shapes belonging to different categories (e.g., rhombuses and rectangles) may share some characteristics, or *attributes*, (e.g., having four sides and four angles.) They went on to learn that these shared attributes can define a larger category. Rhombuses, rectangles and squares, for example, all have four sides and four angles, making them all part of the larger *quadrilateral* category.

Fifth graders build on this idea. They understand that the shapes within the larger quadrilateral category can be arranged in subgroups. Once shapes are arranged in subcategories, children see that any attributes that apply to the larger group also apply to each shape in the subgroups. Parallelograms, for example, have two sets of equal, parallel sides. Rectangles are a subcategory of parallelograms, which means that rectangles must also have two sets of equal, parallel sides.

The big idea here is that all four-sided figures are quadrilaterals, but they can be further classified based on their characteristics, or attributes. Each time a figure is further classified, it maintains its former classifications, belonging to more than one category, and having all of the attributes of each category it belongs to. This means, for example, that a rectangle has parallel opposite sides because a rectangle is a parallelogram and parallelograms have opposite sides that are parallel.

©2016 Conceptual Learning Associates

Example:

Quadrilateral

Any closed (begins and ends at the same point) figure with four sides.

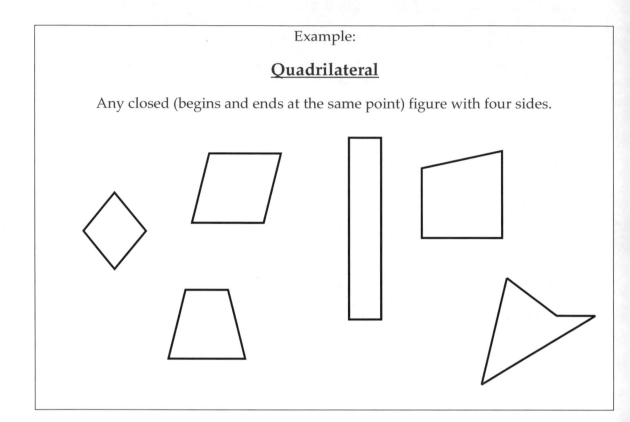

©2016 Conceptual Learning Associates

Subcategories

(of quadrilaterals)

	4-right angles	4-equal sides	*at least* 1-pair of parallel sides	opposite sides parallel	opposite sides equal	opposite angles are equal
trapezoid	●	●	✓	●	●	●
parallelogram	●	●	✓	✓	✓	✓
rectangle	✓	●	✓	✓	✓	✓
rhombus	●	✓	✓	✓	✓	✓
square	✓	✓	✓	✓	✓	✓

KEY

✓ denotes this is ALWAYS true

● denotes this is SOMETIMES true

- Parallelograms are quadrilaterals with 2 pairs of opposite parallel sides
- Rectangles are quadrilaterals with four right angles
- Rhombuses are quadrilaterals with equal side lengths
- Squares are quadrilaterals with equal side lengths and four right angles

©2016 Conceptual Learning Associates

Classifying Figures

<u>Learning standard 5.G.4 says:</u>

Classify two-dimensional figures in a hierarchy based on properties.

<u>What it means:</u>

Children in fifth grade use what they understand about the attributes (characteristics) of two dimensional figures to group and rank them. This ranking, called a *hierarchy*, is most commonly applied to the classification of four sided figures. Children build on what they first worked on in third grade; understanding the "umbrella term" *quadrilateral* to mean any closed two-dimensional figure that contains four sides. There are many four-sided figures that children are familiar with, and in fifth grade they are able rank them in a hierarchy. To do this they rely on their understanding of attributes and subgroups. Each shape students place in the hierarchy must share the attributes of all of the shapes that came before it. For this reason, the hierarchy is created using the broadest term, quadrilateral, first. Attributes become more and more specific as the hierarchy continues to build.

©2016 Conceptual Learning Associates

Example:

Quadrilaterals

- Closed polygons with four sides

Trapezoids (inclusive)

- *At least* 1 pair of parallel sides

Parallelograms

- 2 pairs of opposite parallel sides

Rectangles

- 2 pairs of parallel sides
- 2 pairs of congruent (equal length) sides
- 4 right (90 degree) angles

Rhombuses

- 4 congruent (equal length) sides
- Can have 4 right angles
- Can have opposite angles of equal measure (2 are acute and 2 obtuse)

Squares

- 4 congruent (equal length) sides
- 4 right (90 degree) angles

119

©2016 Conceptual Learning Associates

As the chart is read from top to bottom, the definitions of the figures become more and more specialized. The figures are arranged to show that each one also "fits" into the categories above it. A parallelogram, for example, can also be classified as a trapezoid and quadrilateral because it meets those specifications.

When reading the chart, it is important to keep these guidelines in mind:

- Once a quadrilateral has at least one set of parallel lines it becomes a trapezoid.
- Having two sets of parallel lines creates a parallelogram.
- Rectangles and Rhombuses are two specific types of parallelograms:
  - Rectangles have four right angles, but can have two sets of different length sides.
  - Rhombuses have four equal length sides, may have 4 right angles, or 2 equal measure acute, and 2 equal measure obtuse angles
- Squares are both special rectangles and special rhombuses:
  - Squares have four right angles, like rectangles.
  - Squares have four equal-length sides, like rhombuses.

Following the arrows UP from each shape will allow you to find all of the additional categories each figure ALWAYS belongs to. A rectangle, for example, is always a parallelogram. Likewise, a square is always a rectangle.

A rectangle, however, isn't always a square. Sometimes a rectangle will have 4 equal length sides, but it doesn't have to. Following the arrows DOWN from each shape will show you the "sometimes" relationships between the figures. A parallelogram, for example, is sometimes a rectangle. Likewise, a rhombus is sometimes a square.

©2016 Conceptual Learning Associates

It often takes a little while for children to understand the "sometimes" relationships between the figures. Fifth graders must rely on reasoning and their understanding of the definition of each shape to answer questions like these:

- **Is a rhombus a parallelogram?**

  Yes, always.

- **Is a parallelogram a square?**

  Sometimes.

- **Is a rectangle a square?**

  Sometimes

- **Is a rectangle a rhombus? ***

  Sometimes (when the rectangle is a square).

  *To answer this question children extend their reasoning skills to include the understanding that, although they are not directly related to each other, rectangles and rhombuses are both related to squares.

©2016 Conceptual Learning Associates

GRADE 5- MEASUREMENT AND DATA

By meeting the learning standards in this section, fifth grade children will show that they:

Know how to convert between measurement units.

Can create a line plot to display measurement data.

Can interpret data displayed on a line plot and solve word problems related to the data.

Converting Measurement Units

Learning standard 5.MD.1 says:

Convert among different-sized standard measurement units within a given measurement system (e.g., convert 5 cm to 0.05 m), and use these conversions in solving multi-step, real world problems.

What it means:

Children first worked with converting measurement units in fourth grade, converting larger units to smaller units (for example, feet to inches or hours to minutes). They represented the measurements in 2-column tables, identified the pattern of the table, and eventually learned to apply the pattern's rule (for example, 12 x any # of feet = total # of inches) to any number of larger units to find the total number of smaller ones.

In fifth grade, children continue to work with measurement conversions, extending their work to include smaller to larger unit conversions (for example, centimeters to meters or feet to yards). They use the familiar two-column table representation as well as their understanding of multiplication and division to make these conversions (for example, multiplying by 3 to convert feet to yards and dividing by 3 to convert yards to feet).

Fifth graders also use their understanding of different kinds of numbers to represent equivalent measurements. They recognize, for example, that $4\frac{1}{2}$ liters can also be represented as 4.5 liters or 4500 milliliters.

When converting between units in the metric system, children in fifth grade recognize that the base-ten relationship between the units is the same as the relationship that exists between columns on a place value chart. They use this relationship to easily multiply and divide by powers of ten in order to make these conversions.

Fifth grade children use all of these conversion strategies in order to solve word problems where more than one unit is used. They understand that in order to solve these problems, one of the units must be converted to match the other, so that the numbers in the problem can be worked with, and the solution will make sense.

123

Example:

Create a table to show the rule for converting meters to centimeters.

IN	OUT	
meters (m)	centimeters (cm)	number pairs
1	100	(1, 100)
2	a	(2, a)
3	b	(3, b)
c	400	(c, 400)
5	d	(5, d)

A child solving this problem would use the information from the first line of the table to replace the variables in the other lines with the missing numbers. She might reason like this, "If there are 100 centimeters in 1 meter, then 2 meters would have 200 centimeters, 3 meters would have 300….etc. The number of centimeters is 100 times greater than the number of meters. I just multiply the number of meters by 100 to find the number of centimeters."

She might go on to think, "To find the value of c, I need to go from centimeters to meters. The number of meters is 100 times less than the number of centimeters so I need to divide."

To complete the table, this child used reasoning and her understanding of place value. Since the metric system is a "base-ten" or "decimal" system, like our number system, these conversions are simple for children to complete mentally.

How can you use this table to find the number of centimeters in 18 meters?

©2016 Conceptual Learning Associates

To answer this question, a child might think, "I can just triple (multiply by 3) the number of centimeters in 6 meters. Three times 600 is 1,800 so the answer is 1,800 centimeters."

Or

A child might simply apply the rule of the table:

# of meters x 100 = # of centimeters

IN x *100* = *OUT* (Rule: x 100)

18 x 100 = 1,800 centimeters

How can you use this table to find the number of meters in 25 centimeters?

To answer this question, a child might think, "I am converting from a smaller unit (centimeters) to a larger one (meters) so there will be fewer of them. Since meters are 100 times smaller than centimeters, I need to divide by 100."

# of centimeters ÷ 100 = # of meters

OUT ÷ 100 = *IN* (Rule: ÷ 100)

25 ÷ 100 = .25 meters

This child used her understanding of place value and decimal numbers in order to complete this division. Fifth graders understand that each column on a place value chart is 10 times less than the one to its left. To divide by 100, a number shifts two tens to the right. 25 becomes .25 when it is divided by 100 and shifts two places left on the place value chart.

©2016 Conceptual Learning Associates

Example:

Chris has a 5-foot long by 1-foot wide space on his bedroom wall to decorate. The three posters he wants to hang up are 2.5 feet long, 15 inches long, and 1 foot 6 inches long. All of the posters are 12 inches wide. Does Chris have enough room to hang all three posters with no space between them?

To solve this problem a child might think, "Some of the measurements are feet and some are inches. I need to convert one of them to match the other so that I can work with the numbers."

He or she might go on to reason, "The wall space is 5 feet long. Since 5 x 12 is 60, I know the space is 60 inches long."

"Next I need to see how much space the posters will take up. Since 2.5 is the same as two and a half, I can add 12 inches + 12 inches + 6 inches to find the number of inches the first poster needs. It needs 30 inches of space."

"It says that the second poster is 15 inches long, so I don't have to do any conversions for that one."

"The third poster is 1 foot and 6 inches. That's 12 + 6, or 18 inches."

$$30 + 15 + 18 = ?$$

$$30 + 15 + 15 + 3 = 63$$

He only has 60 inches of space but the posters total 63 inches.

Chris doesn't have enough room to hang all of the posters.

©2016 Conceptual Learning Associates

Creating Line Plots

Learning standard 5.MD.2 says:

Make a line plot to display a data set of measurements in fractions of a unit (1/2, 1/4, 1/8). Use operations on fractions for this grade to solve problems involving information presented in line plots. For example, given different measurements of liquid in identical beakers, find the amount of liquid each beaker would contain if the total amount in all the beakers were redistributed equally.

What it means:

In fourth grade children measured groups of objects to the nearest $\frac{1}{8}$, $\frac{1}{4}$, $\frac{1}{2}$, or whole unit. They recorded their measurements to make *a set of data*, and then *created a line plot to display their data*. A line plot starts as a number line, with the numbers written under the marks. X's are placed above the number marks to represent the pieces of data (the measurements). One X is used to represent one piece of data. *It's important that the X's placed in the line plot are the same size and that they're spaced evenly.*

127

Example:

Measure the length of 10 crayons to the nearest $\frac{1}{8}$ inch. Create a line plot to display your data set.

A child might create a line plot like the one below to complete this task:

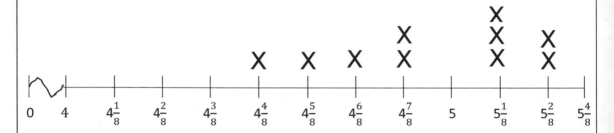

It is important for the interval (the space between the numbers), in this case $\frac{1}{8}$ of an inch, to be equally-spaced across the line plot.

Notice that the intervals on this line plot are all expressed in terms of eighths. Using the same fraction across the line plot helps children create equal intervals. When measuring, however, they may use half- and quarter-inch fractions. Most children will realize that they must convert all of their measurements to eighths in order to plot the data. ($\frac{1}{2}$ for example, will need to be plotted as $\frac{4}{8}$.)

Children can use the information in this graph to answer questions such as:

- What is the length of crayon that appeared the most? What is the total length of these crayons?
- What is the length of the shortest crayon that you measured? What is the difference in length of the longest and shortest crayons?
- How many crayons measured between $4\frac{5}{8}$ and $5\frac{1}{8}$ inches long?

One X in this case represents one crayon, making it easy to see from this line plot that more $5\frac{1}{8}$ inch crayons were measured than any other size.

©2016 Conceptual Learning Associates

Example:

Each X on the line plot below represents the amount of sand, in pounds, that one bucket contains. If the sand were redistributed so that each of the buckets had exactly the same amount, how much sand would be in each bucket?

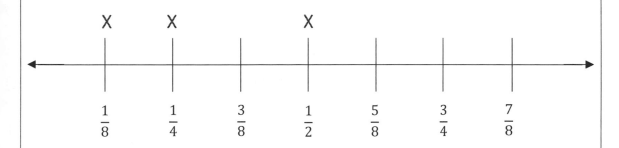

To solve this problem, one child thinks, "There are three buckets. So the sand in each bucket needs to be divided by 3. Then I can add up the amounts that are put in each bucket."

$$\frac{1}{8} \div 3 = \frac{1}{24} \qquad \frac{1}{4} \div 3 = \frac{1}{12} \qquad \frac{1}{2} \div 3 = \frac{1}{6}$$

$$\frac{1}{24} + \frac{1}{12} + \frac{1}{6} = \frac{1}{24} + \frac{2}{24} + \frac{4}{24} = \frac{7}{24}$$

Each bucket will have $\frac{7}{24}$ pound of sand.

©2016 Conceptual Learning Associates

Another child might solve the same problem differently, by thinking, "I can add to find the total amount of sand in all of the buckets. Then I can divide the total amount by 3 so that I end up with the equal amount in each bucket."

$$\frac{1}{8} + \frac{1}{4} + \frac{1}{2}$$

"I need to make the denominators the same so that I can add these fractions. Fourths and halves can both be converted to eighths."

$$\frac{1}{8} + \frac{2}{8} + \frac{4}{8} = \frac{7}{8}$$

"There are 3 buckets so I need to divide by 3."

$$\frac{7}{8} \div 3 = \frac{7}{24}$$

Each bucket will have $\frac{7}{24}$ pound of sand.

©2016 Conceptual Learning Associates

GRADE 5- COORDINATE GRAPHING

By meeting the learning standards in this section, fifth grade children will show that they:

Understand that two perpendicular number lines form the x-axis and y-axis on a coordinate plane.

Can use what they understand about plotting points and graphing to solve word problems.

Are able to use patterns and rules to create and graph ordered pairs on a coordinate plane.

Exploring the Coordinate Plane

Learning standard 5.G.1 says:

Use a pair of perpendicular number lines, called axes, to define a coordinate system, with the intersection of the lines (the origin) arranged to coincide with the 0 on each line and a given point in the plane located by using an ordered pair of numbers, called its coordinates. Understand that the first number indicates how far to travel from the origin in the direction of one axis, and the second number indicates how far to travel in the direction of the second axis, with the convention that the names of the two axes and the coordinates correspond (e.g., x-axis and x-coordinate, y-axis and y-coordinate).

What it means:

Everything fifth graders learn about graphing on a coordinate plane starts with their understanding of the number line. By now they understand that number lines can go in any direction, with any orientation: left/right (horizontal), up/down (vertical), on a slant (diagonal). When children are introduced to the coordinate plane, they recognize that it is created by two perpendicular number lines (number lines that form a 90 degree angle), called *axes*. The point at which the number lines meet is "0" on each of them. This point, the *ordered pair* (0,0), is also known as *the origin*.

Children in fifth grade know that the numbers on each number line enable them to locate points on the grid that the number lines create. When they plot a point using an ordered pair, children understand that the first number in the pair tells them how far from the origin to travel on one axis (number line) and the second number tells how far to travel on the other axis. The point on the grid where these two points meet is where the new point is plotted.

The important point children must remember is that the first number in an ordered pair is called the *x-coordinate*, and always corresponds with the *x-axis (the x number line)*. The second number in the ordered pair, the *y-coordinate*, always corresponds with the *y-axis (the y number line)*.

©2016 Conceptual Learning Associates

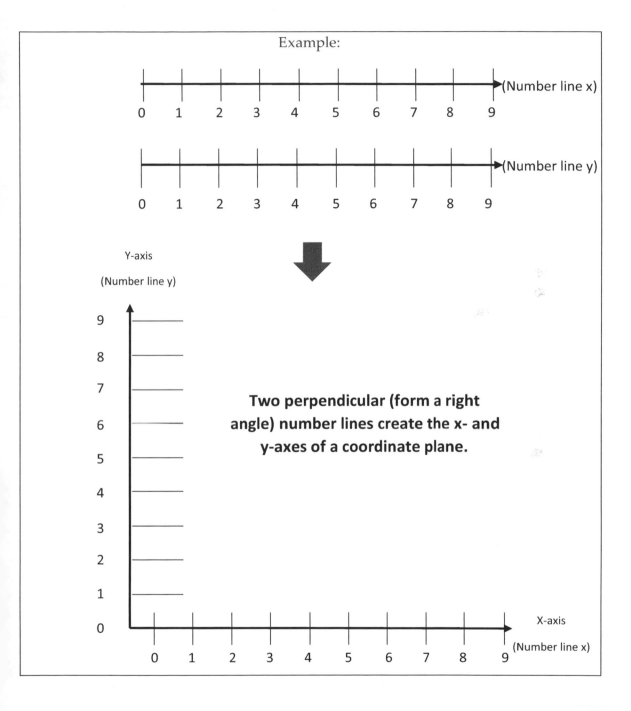

Example:

Two perpendicular (form a right angle) number lines create the x- and y-axes of a coordinate plane.

©2016 conceptual Learning Associates

Graphing Points to Solve Problems

Learning standard 5.G.2 says:

Represent real world and mathematical problems by graphing points in the first quadrant of the coordinate plane, and interpret coordinate values of points in the context of the situation.

What it means:

Children in fifth grade use what they understand about a coordinate grid to represent and solve word problems. To solve these problems children use their understanding of "ordered pairs". An ordered pair contains 2 numbers, called "x" and "y" coordinates. The "x" coordinate is always the first number (on the left) in the pair, and the "y" number is always the second number (on the right). Each pair represents a point on the corresponding number line (the "x" number corresponds with the x axis, and the "y" number corresponds with the y axis.)

To plot a point using an ordered pair, children follow this sequence:

- They first look at the x coordinate. Beginning at "0" on the x axis (the horizontal number line), children count over to the right the same number of spaces as the x coordinate.
- Next, from that spot, children count up the number of spaces denoted by the y coordinate. Children know that they don't have to go back to the "0" before counting up because "zero" on the y axis (the vertical number line) is still "zero" no matter how far to the right they move.
- After counting "over" for the x coordinate, and "up" for the y coordinate, children know they have located the spot where they should plot the new point.
- Once a point is plotted, or drawn in, children label it with either the ordered pair, or with a single upper case letter.

So, for example, to plot the ordered pair (4, 7), a child would place his/her pencil point at zero and count four spaces to the right. Next he or she would count up 7 spaces. After counting up, he or she draws in, or "plots" the point. Finally, the point gets labeled.

134

©2016 Conceptual Learning Associates

This procedure is the same whether children are finding and plotting points from given ordered pairs, or writing the ordered pair for a point they have been given. In either case, children understand that they must ALWAYS move to the side for the x coordinate, BEFORE moving up for the y coordinate.

Eventually, children develop a new understanding of x- and y- coordinates. The big idea here is that each coordinate number (the x number and y number in an ordered pair) is actually a measurement of how far away from the other axis a point is. This means that the x coordinate of any point is actually a measure of distance from the y-axis. Likewise, the y coordinate is a measure of distance above the x-axis.

> To better understand this, let's look again at our example of the ordered pair (4, 7). To find the x coordinate, children begin at 0 and count 4 places to the right on the x-axis....but they are also moving 4 places FROM the y-axis at the same time! To find the y coordinate, children next count 7 places up the y-axis ....moving 7 places ABOVE the x-axis!

This relationship between the *x and y coordinates* and the *x and y axes* is a major understanding for fifth graders, which only develops AFTER children have a lot of experience and practice plotting points using the sequence on the previous page. Over time, children start to "see" that when plotting each coordinate they are moving away from the opposite axis.

Problems children solve using ordered pairs and the coordinate plane might include map problems involving finding locations or requiring children to determine distances.

When solving these problems, children might follow a series of directions or clues to plot points and "find" items or destinations. Fifth graders understand that the same coordinate grid can represent many different situations depending on the context of the problem they are solving.

©2016 conceptual Learning Associates

Example:

Plot point Z six units from the y-axis and three units above the x-axis. Give the ordered pair for point z.

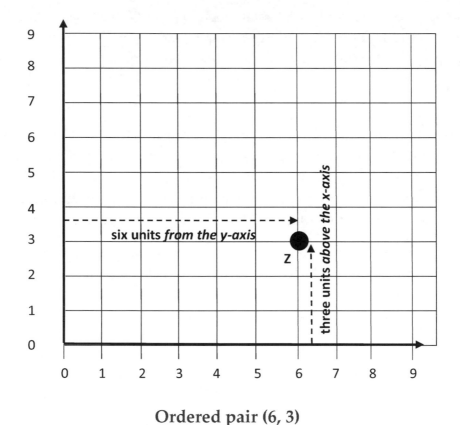

Ordered pair (6, 3)

©2016 Conceptual Learning Associates

Coordinate Plane Graphing

Learning standard 5.OA.3 says:

Generate two numerical patterns using two given rules. Identify apparent relationships between corresponding terms. Form ordered pairs consisting of corresponding terms from the two patterns, and graph the ordered pairs on a coordinate plane. For example, given the rule "Add 3" and the starting number 0, and given the rule "Add 6" and the starting number 0, generate terms in the resulting sequences, and observe that the terms in one sequence are twice the corresponding terms in the other sequence. Explain informally why this is so.

What it means:

In fifth grade children build on the work with patterns and tables they did in earlier grades. This work is extended as children create tables that follow given rules, and then use the numbers in the tables to create ordered pairs (x and y numbers that represent a point on a graph). Using two different rules, one for each column of the table, (such as "Add 3" and "Add 6") and the same starting point for each (zero, for example) children create two sequences of numbers. Then they match up the terms in order to create pairs of numbers. (The first number in each column make up the first pair, the second two numbers become the second pair, etc.) Once they have created these ordered pairs, children graph them on a coordinate plane.

Fifth graders understand that when graphing ordered pairs the first number in the pair is the "x" term and the second one is the "y" term. Beginning at 0 they move to the right along the x axis (horizontally) just as they would on a number line until they reach the correct number. Next they move vertically up the y axis to the correct number. The point at which the x number and y number meet is where they plot (draw) the point.

When working with the number pairs, also called *ordered pairs,* children recognize that the **relationship** between the two numbers in each pair remains constant. In the case of our example, ("Add 3" for the first number and "Add 6" for the second number) children recognize that the "y" coordinate (the second number) is always double the "x" coordinate (the first number). Children see the relationship, and are able to explain that the reason it exists is because the number being added in the "y" rule is double the number in the "x" rule.

137

Example:

Using the two rules below, create a set of ordered pairs that can be plotted on a coordinate plane.

Beginning at 0, follow the rule "Add 3" to create a sequence of 5 terms.

A child solving this problem might think this way, "I just have to start at 0 and add three. That's 3! Then I just have to add three more to each number. Three and three more is 6. Six and three more is 9. If I keep adding 3 my list of terms will be: 0, 3, 6, 9, 12. Since this is the first rule, these terms will be my x-coordinates."

Beginning at 0, follow the rule "Add 6" to create a second sequence of 5 terms.

The thinking might continue like this, "I start at 0 and add six to each term. Zero plus six is 6. Six plus 6 is 12, and 6 more is 18, etc. So my sequence will be: 0, 6, 12, 18, 24. This is the second rule, so these terms will be my y-coordinates."

Match up the numbers in both lists to create a list of number pairs.

Finally this child might reason this way," I can make a table out of the terms I created. I can line up the first x term with the first y term, the second x with the second y, etc. Each set of terms makes an ordered pair that I can plot."

x-number	y-number	Ordered pairs
0	0	(0, 0)
3	6	(3, 6)
6	12	(6, 12)
9	18	(9, 18)
12	24	(12, 24)

©2016 Conceptual Learning Associates

Once fifth graders have mastered the creation and plotting of ordered pairs, the focus shifts to the rule they used to create the pairs. Children come to understand that when they know the rule, also known as the "relationship between x and y", they can use it to write any number of ordered pairs. These pairs can be plotted on a graph, and the points connected to create the line that is represented by the rule. Based on what they understand about patterns, children know that they can use the rule to extend the line they create in either direction.

Example:

Graph and draw the line that is represented by the rule "y is twice x"

$(y = 2x)$.

A child solving this problem might start by thinking, "Since y is twice x any number I use for x just has to be doubled to become the y number. I can use that rule to create these pairs:

(1, 2)	(5, 10)
(2, 4)	(6, 12)
(3, 6)	(9, 18)*
(4, 8)	(11, 22)*

*Children will probably not need to plot all of these points in order to connect them and create the line. What's important here is that they are able to recognize when additional points (such as (9, 18) and (12, 24) in the following diagram) will or will not fall on the line that they have created.

Children might be asked, for example, if ordered pair (31, 60) falls on the line $y = 2x$. They would be expected to know that it does not fall on the line because 60 (y) is not equal to 2 x 31 (x).

©2016 conceptual Learning Associates

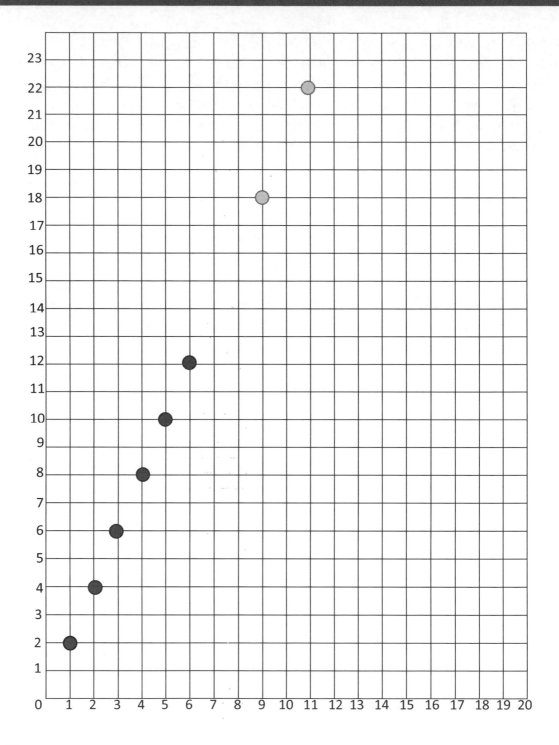

©2016 Conceptual Learning Associates

© 2016 Conceptual Learning Associates

© 2016 Conceptual Learning Associates